The Doctor Writes

a note about the editor

S. O. Waife, the collector of the papers for this anthology, is an Associate in Medicine, Indiana University Medical School; Associate Physician, Indianapolis General Hospital; Physician, Medical Department, Lilly Research Laboratories; a diplomate of the American Board of Internal Medicine; and a fellow of the American College of Physicians. He is Editor-in-Chief of the *Journal of Clinical Nutrition,* Editor of *American Lectures in Metabolism* (monographs), and Editor of *Physician's Bulletin,* a publication of Eli Lilly and Company. He has frequently contributed to periodicals and textbooks.

The Doctor Writes

An Anthology of the Unusual
in Current Medical Literature

edited by

S. O. Waife, M.D., F.A.C.P.

Grune & Stratton   New York   1954

Library of Congress Catalog Card Number 54–7869

Printed and bound in U.S.A.

Introduction

THE IDEA for this book originated in a rather casual way. While sorting a large number of medical reprints into folders with formidable titles, I soon found a group which I had enjoyed reading but which did not fall into the usual "scientific" classification. These were reprints of papers on diversified medical and perimedical topics (often with intriguing titles) which particularly lent themselves to rereading because of the timeless quality of the subject matter or the fine literary style of the author. I thought a collection of some of the outstanding articles of 1953 would be of interest to others. This little anthology is the result.

This is a personal selection. Obviously, like any collection of best poems, plays, or paintings, they will not be the favorite selection of every reader. However, it is hoped the wide variety of topics discussed will offer something of interest to everyone. Furthermore, in selecting these articles, I have been guided by three principles: the paper should be on an interesting subject, it should be well written, and above all, it should be a *pleasure* to read.

The medical literature of today is so vast that no one can hope to even scan all publications for the tables of contents. I am certain that many exceptionally fine contributions have escaped my surveillance. To their authors I offer sincerest regrets at not being able to enjoy the product of their pens. Furthermore, limitation of space prohibits the inclusion of *all* articles which I thought would prove entertaining to the reader. In the selection of those to be included, personal bias obviously crept in. It was gratifying, however, to realize how many good papers appear in the medical press every month.

Medical communications often end with a conclusion. This introduction ends with the hope that the contents of this anthology will afford emotional pleasure, intellectual profit, and spiritual peace to the reader.

S. O. WAIFE

Indianapolis, 1954

Acknowledgments

Grateful acknowledgement is made to the following for their cooperation and permission to reprint the articles in this volume:

To the Editors and Publishers of the A.M.A. Archives of Dermatology and Syphilology, the A.M.A. Archives of Internal Medicine, the Bulletin of the History of Medicine, Circulation Research, Cleveland Clinic Quarterly, the International Journal of Psycho-Analysis, the Journal of the American Medical Association, the Journal of Clinical Endocrinology and Metabolism, the Journal of Laboratory and Clinical Medicine, the Journal of Medical Education, the Lancet, Obstetrics & Gynecology, Postgraduate Medicine, the Psychoanalytic Review, the Rhode Island Medical Journal, and Texas Reports of Biology and Medicine:

And to the authors of the papers; namely, Robert S. Alexander, Ph.D., William Bennett Bean, M.D., Richard D. Bryant, M.D., C. L. Buxton, M.D., Sir John Charles, M.D., F.R.C.P., Kenneth Mark Colby, M.D., Noah D. Fabricant, M.D., Nathan Flaxman, M.D., Walter Freeman, M.D., Ph.D., Otto Glasser, Ph.D., Allan Gregg, M.D., Joseph V. Klauder, M.D., Louis A. M. Krause, M.D., Joost A. M. Meerloo, M.D., Nancy Procter-Gregg, John W. Todd, M.D., M.R.C.P., and W. Barry Wood, Jr., M.D.

The Editor is also happy to acknowledge his appreciation to Miss Carol-Joyce Howell and Miss Mary Sibbach for their valuable assistance.

Contents

OF MEN AND MEDICINE

———————1———————

Sherlock Holmes as a Dermatologist

With Remarks on the Life of Dr. Joseph Bell and the Sherlockian Method of Teaching

JOSEPH V. KLAUDER, M.D.

But if truth is stranger than fiction, then fantasy must sometimes attain astonishing heights of verisimilitude.—American Scientist 40:380, 1952.

BEFORE DISCUSSING Sherlock Holmes as a dermatologist, and reporting the clinic he conducts and the Sherlockian method of teaching, it is pertinent to discuss his teacher, Dr. Joseph Bell (1837–1911).

Dr. Joseph Bell, who entered the medical school of the University of Edinburgh in 1821, later becoming professor of surgery, came from a distinguished family of physicians. His kinsmen were enrolled as members of the Royal College of Surgery, either a Benjamin or Joseph, for 140 years commencing in 1771.[1]

Bell was an excellent surgeon, a prolific writer, and popular as a teacher. His lectures and clinics in which he presented patients with a variety of diseases were always crowded. He would astound his students with his intuitive powers and keen observation, skill in eliciting facts and in deduction. He emphasized the importance of training the student's observant faculties. "Eyes and ears which can see and hear, memory to record at once . . . precise and intelligent recognition and appreciation of minor differences as the essential factor in all successful medical diagnosis." [2] In his stress on the importance of observation he wrote: "I

Read at a meeting of (Sherlock Holmes Society) The Sons of The Copper Beeches of Philadelphia, Scion Society of the Baker Street Irregulars.

Reprinted from A. M. A. ARCHIVES OF DERMATOLOGY AND SYPHILOLOGY Vol. 68, pp. 363–377, October 1953 always impressed over and over again upon my students the vast importance of little distinctions, the endless significance of the trifles." "Nearly every handicraft writes its sign-manual on the hands. The scars of the miner differ from those of the quarryman. The carpenter's callosities are not those of the mason. . . . The soldier and sailor differ in gait. Accent helps you to district and, to an educated ear, almost to county. . . . With a woman, especially the observant doctor can often tell what part of her body she is going to talk about." [3]

Throughout his life he continued to amaze his circle through his keen observation and deduction. His daughter, Mrs. C. C. Stisted, recalls: "He would tell us where all the other passengers in the carriage were from, where they were going, and something of their occupation and habits. All this without having spoken to them. When he verified his observations, we thought him a magician." [3]

A. Conan Doyle (1859–1930) when a student at Edinburgh (1876–1881) was much impressed by the powers of observation and deductions of Joseph Bell, which inspired him to create Sherlock Holmes the prototype of Dr. Bell.[4] A. Conan Doyle writes [5]: "But the most notable of the characters whom I met was one Joseph Bell, surgeon at the Edinburgh Infirmary. Bell was a very remarkable man in body and mind. He was thin, wiry, dark,[6] with a high nosed acute face, penetrating grey eyes, angular shoulders, and a jerky way of walking. His voice was high and discordant. He was a very skilled surgeon, but his strong point was diagnosis, not only of disease, but of occupation and character. For some reason which I have never understood he singled out from the drove of students who frequented his wards and made me his out-patient clerk, which meant that I had to array his out-patients, make simple notes of their cases, and then show them in, one by one, to the large room in which Bell sat in state surrounded by his dressers and students.

"Then I had ample chance of studying his methods and of noticing that he often learned more of the patient by a few quick glances than I had done by my questions. Occasionally the results were very dramatic, though there were times when he blundered. Case No. 1 would step up.

" 'I see,' said Mr. Bell, 'you're suffering from drink. You even carry a flask in the inside breast pocket of your coat.'

"Another case would come forward.

" 'A cobbler, I see.' Then he would turn to the students and point out to them that the inside of the knee of the man's trousers was worn. That was where the man had rested the lapstone, a peculiarity only found in cobblers.

"In one of his best cases he said to a civilian patient, 'Well, my man, you've served in the army.' 'Aye, sir.' 'Not long discharged?' 'No, sir.' 'A Highland regiment?' 'Aye, sir.' 'A non-commissioned officer?' 'Aye, sir.' 'Stationed at Barbados?' 'Aye, sir.' [7] 'You see, gentlemen,' he would explain, 'the man was a respectful man but did not remove his hat. They do not in the army, but he would have learned civilian ways had he long been discharged. He has an air of authority and he is obviously Scottish. As to Barbados, his complaint is elephantiasis, which is West Indian and not British.'

"All this impressed me very much. He was continually before me—his sharp, piercing eyes, eagle nose, and striking features. There he would sit in his chair with fingers together—he was very dexterous with his hands—and just look at the man or woman before him. When I took my degree and went to Africa the remarkable individuality and discriminating tact of my old master made a deep and lasting impression on me, though I had not the faintest idea that it would one day lead me to forsake medicine for story writing."

Prior to Bell and contemporaneous with him there were other illustrious physicians who excelled in naming the patient's occupation at first glance. Tardieu,[8] in his comprehensive discussion of occupational stigmas, attributes this attribute to Corvisart (1755–1821), of the French School of Medicine, and his pupil Dupuytren (1777–1835), who, like Bell, was a renowned surgeon and diagnostician, and Trousseau (1801–1865), a French internist.

George Henry Fox,[9] in his "Reminiscences," discusses the keen observation of Hebra (1816–1880) and his vivid description of cutaneous diseases. "He rarely asked his patient any questions, but a hasty glance would usually enable him to tell more about the case than any one of his students would elicit by a lengthy catechism. . . . He would say, 'This man is a tailor,' and we soon found that he discovered this fact by feeling the needle pricks on the roughened forefinger. A hatter he recognized by some peculiar callus on the ball of the thumb. He could always guess the age and weight of a patient with unerring accuracy and tell us what province of Austria he came from." "While waiting for a patient to remove a bandage from his leg, Hebra casually glanced at him and remarked, 'This man is a Croat, 55 years of age, has pulmonary tuberculosis, and is a tailor by occupation.' . . . Wouldn't you know he was a tailor? Look at that little strip of drab cloth he has tied around the bandage. Tailors use that stuff for vest linings.'"

A. Conan Doyle's training under Dr. Bell is apparent in many of his Sherlock Holmes' stories. The following is a good example. In the "Adventures of the Norwood Builder," when a frantic young man burst into the room on Baker Street and announced himself as John McFarlane, Sherlock Holmes lazily replied, "You mention your name as if I should recognize it, but I assure you that, beyond the obvious facts that you are a bachelor, a solicitor, a Freemason, and an asthmatic, I know nothing whatever about you."

Campbell [10] reviews ample evidence in the Sherlock Holmes' stories to show that A. Conan Doyle had a "very good knowledge of medicine." "He was certainly an acute observer, and it is difficult to see why he was not an outstanding success in practice. . . ."

As an aid to A. Conan Doyle in his fascinating method of identifying the many varied characters that visited Baker Street, there were available in his era a number of medical references. These concerned marks of occupation, dysharmony of physique, deformities and other structural changes incident to occupation [11] (to wit the large right hand of Jabez Wilson indicating manual labor).[12] Tardieu [8] in 1850 (with extensive bibliography) reported on 48 different trades and occupations, and Vernois' [13] (1862) comprehensive study embraced 150 kinds of occupations. Campbell [10] reviews the several publications of Lane [14] (1886–1888) on anatomical changes induced by occupation.

It it doubtful, however, if Doyle needed to resort to the literature in consideration of his training under Bell, his creative mind and vivid imagination.

Figures 1 to 3 (a contribution to Sherlockiana) show marks of occupation and of profession (as discussed in their legends). With the exception of Figure 1 none of these marks are illustrated or discussed by Ronchese [11] or by Schwartz, Tulipan and Peck.[11] The callus shown in Figure 1 is labeled "handwriter's callus" by Ronchese in his text. He records its occurrence from a variety of implements employed in different occupations.

SHERLOCK HOLMES AND DERMATOLOGY

Keen observation, intense inspection of the subject, attention to details and apparent trifles so much emphasized by Sherlock Holmes are particularly pertinent to the dermatologist. It has been appropriately said that in diagnosis of contact dermatitis the dermatologist should be a good detective [17] with "the power of observation and that of deduction." [18] The diagnosis of cutaneous disease is essentially objective, and attention to morphologic and topographical detail (see Case 5) is important.

Indeed medical diagnosis in general is essentially deduction from premises elicited by inspection, examination, and the aid of instruments of precision and laboratory tests. The application of the laws of logic in diagnosis is pertinently discussed by Southard.[19] Diagnosis of cutaneous diseases should be the last to succumb to present trend in clinical medicine of diagnosis by short cuts afforded by a battery of laboratory tests and instrumental study.

It is disturbing when in demonstrating a patient with an eruption covered with scratch marks, a student naively asks the patient does the rash itch, to which Sherlock Holmes would reply, "the great unobservant—who could hardly tell a weaver by his tooth or a compositor by his left thumb.[20]

In presentday emphasis of psychosomatic relations in dermatology, the "sizing-up" of the patient, the demeanor, the quivering voice, the shivering eyelids, the recurring vasomotor flush, the solitary swallow, the emotional background, and environmental circumstances have considerable etiologic significance. This is illustrated in the case of a patient, a young girl who cowered before her mother. A glance sufficed in diagnosis of neurotic excoriations, and the remark of her mother sufficed in explanation, "No one can get a job with a face like that."

Psychiatrists have long had a (Sherlockian) code [21] of the nature and hue of clothing, of hair dress, and of ornamentation as an aid in psychiatric diagnosis. It is germane to this discussion to give this code.[22]

That this code was known to Sherlock Holmes becomes apparent in the case of Miss Morstan,[23] since her dress fitted the depressed female. "The dress was a sombre grayish beige, untrimmed and unbraided, and she wore a small turban of the same dull hue, . . . her lip trembled, her hand quivered and she showed every sign of intense inward agitation." Her depressed state was well explained by "the strange mystery which overhung her life" and correlated her statement, "I have led a retired life." life."

REPORT OF CLINIC CONDUCTED BY SHERLOCK HOLMES

Mimicking his teacher, Dr. Joseph Bell, Sherlock Holmes stares at the patient while "his long white nervous fingers" [24] toy with his magnifying glass. He purposely knows nothing of their history and asks no questions. His method is to inculcate intensive inspection of the patient—the demeanor, the clothing, the skin and the eruption.

CASE 1.—Sherlock Holmes: This child as you can see is about 12 years of age. She is either the oldest or the only child of her parents. She injured her right knee roller skating, I would say about two months ago. Subsequently her eye became inflamed.

Mother: That is extraordinary. How do you know that? She is the oldest child and fell when roller skating ten weeks ago.

Sherlock Holmes: (addressing students). It is apparent that the child has a bilateral swelling of the knees, the right is more swollen. It is nonpainful as is seen from her gait. She has photophobia and lachrymation of one eye. She is a girl between the ages of 8 and 15. These circumstances indicate Clutton's joints—non-painful symmetrical serous synovitis [25] which invariably precedes interstitial keratitis. Like the latter,[26] the disease is at first unilateral and at times appears after injury, followed by involvement of the second knee. The first knee involved is invariably the more swollen one. The course of events requires weeks. Interstitial keratitis, in accordance with Kassowitz' law, most frequently affects the oldest child and in a large percentage of instances the only child. The symmetrical groove depressions on the sides of the fore part of the sole of her shoes suggests the wearing of roller skates.

CASE 2.—Sherlock Holmes: This patient is a retail fish dealer who cut his index finger when cleaning fish, I would say two weeks ago. Sensation of throbbing, burning pain disturbs his sleep and sense of stiffness of some finger joints impairs the use of his hand.

Patient: That is correct, sir, although I cut my finger 12 days ago the redness at its site has disappeared. It appeared on other uninjured fingers and spread onto the back of my hand (Fig. 5). The pain keeps me awake, my fingers feel stiff which interferes with work.

Sherlock Holmes: These circumstances and the distinctive purplish red color of the lesions make the diagnosis of Erysipeloid of Rosenbach [27] obvious.

Student: How do you know the man is not an abattoir worker, a commercial fisherman, or was infected from handling dressed turkeys?

Sherlock Holmes: A commercial fisherman would not be as pale-faced as this patient. The retrogressing remains of the original laceration on the index finger is still apparent. "I have an abnormally acute set of senses,[28] and a faint but incisive scent of fish is apparent. This was confirmed when I noted, as you apparently did not, the few fish scales entangled in the patient's shoe laces," "Perhaps I have trained myself to see what others overlook" [29]—"great issues may hang from a boot lace." [30]

CASE 3.—Patient: I did not come on account of my former skin trouble but I would . . .

Sherlock Holmes: (interrupting the patient and addressing the students) I recall this patient several years back. I note he is still a waiter and has had trouble with his "jalopy." He is not employed in one of our deluxe restaurants. He comes to ask about his flat feet.

Patient: (in a surprised tone) Everything you said is correct.

Sherlock Holmes: The patient's black trousers with their satin band along their sides, his coat and vest of a different texture and color betray his occupation. He is enroute to his place of employment. The black stains around the cuticles of most fingers, apparently of long duration, are not caused by his occupation as a waiter. I guessed he repairs his automobile. No deluxe restaurant would employ a waiter with such hands. Since he is a waiter he is entitled to have flat feet and this presumption is confirmed by the manner of his gait.

CASE 4.—Mother: My little girl, age 3 years, has these scratched areas. The paroxysms of scratching are usually preceded by the statement, "Mother, I am going to scratch." Soon after its onset our Collie dog started to limp. I noticed, however, that when the dog is outside the house the limp disappears.

Sherlock Holmes: You need not tell me that your little girl is the oldest child and the scratching first appeared soon after the birth of your second child.

Mother: That is correct. How do you know that?

Sherlock Holmes: The itching will disappear if you divide your attention between your little girl and the baby. Similarly, resume patting the Collie. (Addressing the class) Much emphasis is now being given to psychosomatic relations in dermatology. The term is a new one—a new label for old wine. My teacher, Dr. Bell, demonstrated a number of instances. He was fond of quoting the American dermatologist, Dr. Hyde of Chicago, who wrote, "The widow must be made to lay aside the heavy crape-veil beneath which her urticaria plays." [31]

I would like to relate a remarkable example of psychosomatic expression that I have encountered.[32] "The person, who we will call Mrs. Seagrave, had been given a curious secondhand ring, snake-shaped, and dull gold. This she took from her finger at night. One night she slept with it on and had a fearsome dream in which she seemed to be pushing off some furious creature which fastened its teeth into her arm. On awakening the pain in the arm continued, and the next day the imprint of a double set of teeth appeared upon the arm, with one tooth of the lower jaw missing. The marks were in the shape of blue-black bruises which had not broken the skin. Mrs. Seagrave informed me that she did not know what made her think the ring had anything to do with the matter, but she took a dislike to the thing and did not wear it for some months, when being on a visit, she took to wearing it again. The same thing happened again, and the lady settled the matter forever by dropping her ring into the hottest corner of the kitchen range.

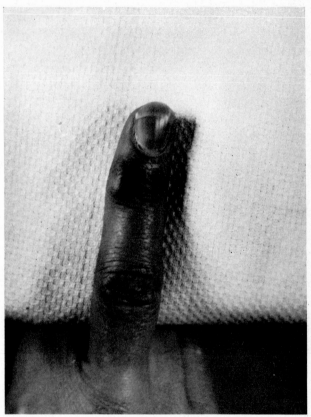

Fig. 1.—Callus on the third finger of an accountant. Its site was at contact with a fountain pen held between the index and third finger.

CASE 5.—Sherlock Holmes: (addressing students) At our last meeting as a test of deductive reasoning, I suggested reading "The Adventure of the Golden Pince-Nez," and to explain, before reaching the end of the story, why, as I maintained, the assassin could not have possibly escaped by walking along the small strip of grass leading from the house to the road.[33]

I wish to emphasize keen observation in diagnosis of an eruption. We need not ask any questions of the patient before us. This method . . . "sharpens the faculties of observation and teaches one where to look and what to look for." [34] The eruption began as a single lesion seen below the right clavicle.

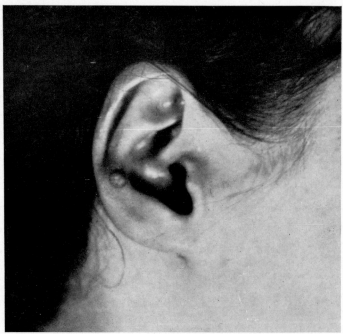

Fig. 2.—A callus on the antihelix of a telephone operator. She used a unilateral ear receiver. A callus first appeared on the right ear, subsequently on the left ear after she changed the receiver to that ear. I have observed similar lesions on nuns from pressure of the starched white headpiece.

This initial lesion, invariably the largest one, is called the "primitive placque" or "herald patch." In this patient it was erroneously diagnosed as ringworm and painted with tincture of iodine. You will note faint trace of such treatment. As a result the lesion became secondarily eczematized, but that should not mislead you. From two or three to ten days, possibly a few weeks, following its onset a full-blown eruption appeared on the trunk. You will observe it is sparing on the neck, exempts the face, and abruptly stops about the midportion of the arms and thighs. Since the eruption is fully developed, its duration is about two weeks. The eruption does not itch, this does not

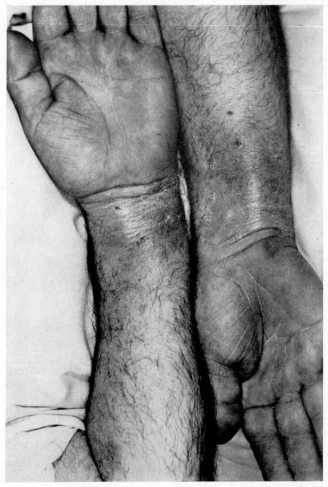

Fig. 3.—Callus-like involvement of the wrists of a baker. The affected skin was dry, thickened, and slightly scaly. With hands pointing upward, the flexor surfaces of the wrists were used to manipulate a thick layer of dough into a roll. The patient also had calluses on the dorsal surfaces of the last three fingers of the right hand. These fingers were used to pry loose a layer of dough from a table, causing friction of the dorsal surfaces against the table.

explain the look of apprehension. The latter is probably caused
by fear that he has contracted a venereal disease and to account
for this anxiety I would conclude the patient is married.

(Sherlock Holmes passes his magnifying glass to a student and

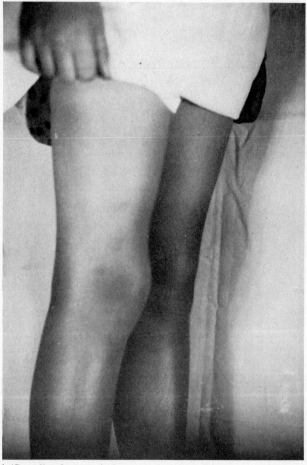

Fig. 4 (Case 1).—Symmetrical serous synovitis (Clutton's joints). The right
knee was the first affected, the swelling appearing after injury when the child
was roller skating and preceding interstitial keratitis. How Sherlock Holmes
determined these circumstances without the aid of history is discussed in
Case 1.

remarks) Closely examine several of the lesions with and without the glass and report everything you see.

Student: The color of the lesions is pink with a slightly reddish tint.

Sherlock Holmes: That is correct, it is usually designated as fawn-colored, chamois skinshade, or salmon pink.

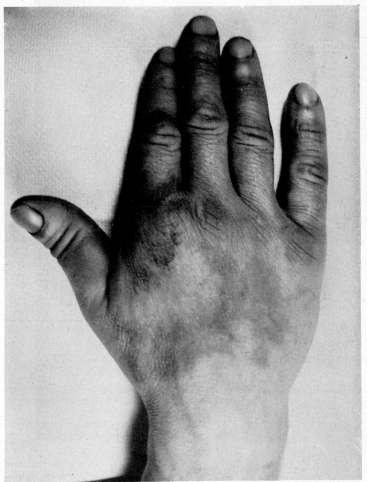

Fig. 5 (Case 2).—Erysipeloid occurring after injury of a finger of a retail fish handler.

Student: The lesions change in configuration on the sides of the neck and sides of the chest from round elsewhere to an oval outline. The lesions are rounded macules varying considerably in size and situated superficially. Their centers are clear but their borders are ringed with a fine, dry scale. These scales are triangular, their bases adherent to the border, their apices are loose and point toward the center of the lesion.

Fig. 6 (Case 7).—Bracelet-like lesions of dermatitis factitia and the "tell tale trickle tail" (an extension from the lesion on the left wrist) produced by Lysol. The patient admitted its use after examination by Sherlock Holmes. How he determined this is discussed in Case 7.

Sherlock Holmes: You have correctly described with one omission the disease called pityriasis rosea.[35] The omission is the wrinkled or crinkled surfaces of the lesions that are likened to crinkled cigarette paper. I hope that what I told you and the manner of telling it together with your minute description of the individual lesions will firmly fix in your mind the characteristic features of the disease.

CASE 6.—The patient was obviously uncomfortable. His face and neck were red and swollen, his eyes almost closed. As the dressing, adherent to the scarlet oozing surfaces of the hands and forearms, was detached Sherlock Holmes looked him over in an abstracted fashion. "He sat silent for a few minutes with his fingertips pressed together and his gaze directed upward toward the ceiling."[36] He suddenly exclaimed.

This young man is an apprentice, he is left-handed, does considerable work reading blue prints or as a draftsman, in addition, experimental work with insulating material including chloronaphthalenes and derivatives of cashew nut shell oil. The

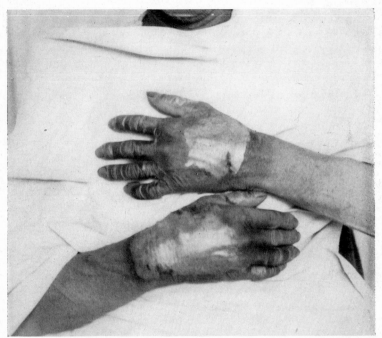

Fig. 7.—Vitiligoid dermatosis in the postdermatic stage of pellagra in an alcoholic addict. Sherlock Holmes's discussion of this patient is embraced in Case 8.

dermatitis has all the earmarks of a contactant cause. It represents an allergic reaction to cashew nut shell oil.

The patient: (in an astonished tone) How on earth do you know that? [37]

Sherlock Holmes: (addressing students) You will observe that his vest is worn across its lower portion from pressure against a table or drafting board. This source is confirmed by the tip of a drawing pen protruding from the vest pocket. He holds the pen in his left hand; that is evidenced by a callus on the side of the middle finger of the left hand (Fig. 1). A sparing number

of lesions of chloracne on the sides of the neck points to recent
exposure to chloronaphthalenes; otherwise they would be much
greater in number. There are traces of varnish on some fingernails. Their thick, tenacious glazed appearance suggests two
compounds—a varnish made from cashew nut shell oil, which
like the chloronaphthalenes are used as insulating and moisture-
resisting agents; the other, phenol formaldehyde resin. The
latter is allergenic; in varnish form it is used as a glue by car-
penters and cabinet makers, which he is not. Chloronaphthalenes
are not allergenic whereas products of cashew nut shell oil are
highly so causing most acute dermatitis of the exposed skin which
the patient has.[38]

I have, as you know, studied marks of identification. "By a
man's fingernails, by his coat-sleeve, by his boots, by his trouser-
knees, by the callosites of his forefinger and thumb, by his
expression, by his shirt-cuffs—by each of these things a man's
calling is plainly revealed. That all united should fail to en-
lighten the competent inquirer in any case is almost inconceivable." [39] I conducted research on the distinction of antemortem
and postmortem bruises [40] and have published studies [41] on "the
influence of a trade upon the form of the hand, with lithotypes
of the hands of slaters, sailors, corkcutters, compositors, weavers
and diamond polishers." [42] "I have made a small study of tattoo
marks and have even contributed to the literature of the subject." [43] . . . "There is no part of the body which varies so much
as the human ear.[44] Each ear, as a rule, is quite distinctive and
differs from other ones. In last year's Anthropological Journal
you will find two short monographs from my pen on the subject." [45]

In a forthcoming publication I will discuss the value of Wood's
fluorescent light in study of marks of violence on the cadaver and
its use in examination of the hands, both antemortem and post-
mortem, as an aid in diagnosis of occupation. The fluorescent
light is of aid in determining the duration of a scar and may be
helpful in determining its source (Ronchese [11]).

CASE 7.—The patient presented four band-like areas of redness
encircling both forearms (shown in Fig. 6). Sherlock Holmes
made an awkward movement whereby he dropped his magnifying
glass at the feet of the patient sitting in front of him. As he

stooped to pick it up his face almost touched the affected right forearm of the patient.

(After dismissing the patient he addressed the students.) The patient has marital difficulties which doubtless explains recent separation from her husband. This is a logical deduction since she recently removed a ring from the fourth finger of the left hand, the conventional site of a wedding ring. Its removal is evidenced by remains of its indentation and slight congestion.

I again wish to emphasize keen observation and deduction in diagnosis of cutaneous diseases. As I have often said, "When you have eliminated all which is impossible, then whatever remains, however improbable, must be the truth." [46] In the case of this patient one can eliminate a spontaneous occurring cutaneous disease. No such disease in human beings [47] has such bizarre outline resembling the stripes of a zebra. Therefore the lesions must have been self-produced. In its production a liquid must have been used. This is apparent since its excess ran down the skin in droplet formation producing small pear-shaped areas of redness extending below the band-like lesions. I hope you observed these pear-shaped areas of redness which we could not discuss in the presence of the patient. They have been aptly called "the tell tale trickle tail." The appearance of acute inflammation suggests that the irritant liquid was recently applied. In that event its odor should be present. To determine this I purposely dropped the magnifying glass and in picking it up I clearly detected a phenolic odor. In all probability Lysol was used.

The diagnosis of self-produced lesion—dermatitis factitia—frequently indicates hysteria and correlating the latter is the vivid hue of her attire. You should have observed that she wore a red hat, purple blouse, a checked skirt of yellow, red and green, and green shoes.

Student: (hesitatingly) Do you think, sir, that the self-produced band-like areas encircling the forearms are a displacement phenomenon to compensate for the removal of the wedding ring that encircles the finger?

Sherlock Holmes: Dermatologists have paid no attention to significance of lesions of dermatitis factitia. I would suggest that you refer to the writings of Freud. You will find ample discussion of configuration pertaining to the symbol of Priapus; in addition you may find discussion of configuration of self-produced cutaneous lesions since Freud attempts to explain the psychodynamics of many curious circumstances.

Second student: (naively) If dermatologists correlated personality types and skin diseases, psychiatrists character and type of clothing, can correlation be made between type of clothing and skin diseases?

Sherlock Holmes: It is likely that dermatologic psychosomaticists may come to such study.

CASE 8.—The patient presented a vitiligoid dermatosis (shown in Fig. 7).

Sherlock Holmes asked a student for the diagnosis.

Student: (proudly and mimicking his teacher) This man was given at place of work a new issue of rubber gloves. About three months after wearing them he and other fellow workers developed this depigmentation. It was erroneously diagnosed vitiligo. It represents what is called occupational leukoderma and is caused by monobenzyl ether of hydroquinone used as an antioxidant in the rubber.

Sherlock Holmes: (sarcastically) Your method of deduction is commendable but your range of observation is not. It did not extend beyond the patient's hands. "You see but you do not observe."—It is a capital mistake to theorize before one has data. Insensibly one begins to twist facts to suit theories, instead of theories to suit facts.[48] "Never trust to general impressions, but concentrate yourself on details." [49] Your premise that all gauntlet dermatoses are from wearing gloves is erroneous. You neglected to consider the classical gloved dermatitis of pellagra which the patient had. It is in the postdermatitic stage characterized by vitiligoid lesions presented by the patient.[50] In confirmation are the rounded pigmentary remains of a pellagrous dermatitis on the elbows, another region of predilection, the perlèche, the bronzing of the face, the dyssebacia, and above all the "corpus delicti" in diagnosis of pellagra—the faint but discernible pigmentary narrow band around the neck with an extension on the manubrium the remains of what is called Casál's (1681–1759) necklace. This is in tribute to a great Spanish physician who first observed and described pellagra in the early part of the 18th Century.

In all probability the cutaneous lesions appeared after prolonged alcoholic debauche. This is supported by his tottering gait, malnutrition, the dull, apathetic appearance, his desolate state and his tremors. During his debauche he drank an incredible amount of liquor and ate . . .

Patient: (interrupting—in a slurring speech). That is right, sir, for weeks I drank a quart or more of whiskey daily and ate only bean soup.

REFERENCES

1. Obituary, Joseph Bell, Edinburgh M. J. 7:454–463, 1911. Saxby, J. M. E.: Joseph Bell. An Appreciation by an Old Friend, Edinburgh and London, Oliphant, Anderson, and Ferrier, 1913.

2. Bell, Joseph: Mr. Sherlock Holmes, preface, in Doyle, A. C.: Study in Scarlet, New Ed., London, Ward, Lock & Bowden, 1894.

3. Wallace, I.: The Incredible Dr. Bell, Sat. Rev. Lit. 31:7–8, 1948.

4. A. Conan Doyle also mentioned Poe's Dupin as another source of Sherlock Holmes. Hespeth Pearson in "Conan Doyle—His Life and Art" suggests that Holmes' precise method first appeared in Voltaire's Zadig.

5. Doyle, A. Conan: Study in Scarlet, preface, New Ed., London, Ward, Lock & Bowden, 1894.

6. It is interesting to note that according to Douglas,[1] Bell's jet black hair went iron gray in three days of anguish during the final illness of his wife. Elsewhere, I recorded similar instances of this phenomenon (Psychogenic Aspects of Skin Diseases, J. Nerv. & Ment. Dis. 84:249–273, 1936).

7. This was reproduced with modification in The Greek Interpreter, p. 504. The page number in this and subsequent similar references is to the Garden City Omnibus edition (The Complete Sherlock Holmes, Garden City Books, Garden City, N. Y.).

8. Tardieu, A.: Mémoire sur les modifications physiques et chimiques que détermine dans certaines parties du corps l'exercice des diverses professions, pour servir à la recherche médicolégale de l'identité, Ann. hyg. 42:388–423, 1894; 43:131–144, 1850.

9. Fox, G. H.: Reminiscences, New York, Froben Press, Inc., 1926, p. 104.

10. Campbell, J.: Sherlock Holmes and Dr. Watson, A Medical Digression for Guy's Hospital Gazette Committee, London, Ash & Co., 1951.

11. In modern literature the volume of Ronchese, F.: Occupational Marks and Other Physical Signs: A Guide to Personal Identification, New York, Grune & Stratton, Inc., 1948, with its many illustrations and comprehensive review of literature is outstanding. The subject is likewise thoroughly discussed by Schwartz, L.; Tulipan, L., and Peck, S. M.: Occupational Diseases of the Skin, Ed. 2, Philadelphia, Lea & Febiger, 1947.

12. The Red Headed League, p. 196.

13. Vernois, M.: De la main des ouvriers et des artisans au point de vue de l'hygiène et de la médecine légale, Ann. hyg. 17:104–190, 1862.

14. Lane, W. A.: A Remarkable Example of the Manner in Which Pressure-Changes in the Skeleton May Reveal the Labour-History of the Individual, J. Anat. 21:385–406, 1886–1887; The Anatomy and Physiology of the Shoe-maker, ibid. 22:593–628, 1887–1888; Some Changes in the Form of Acetabular Cavities, the Spinal Column, and Joints of the Hand, Illustrated by the Anatomy of the Charwoman, Guy's Hosp. Rep. 29:359–367, 1887.

15. Footnote deleted.

16. Footnote deleted.

17. Sutton, R. L., Jr.: Contact Dermatitis: Practical Management and Identification of Cause Without Patch Testing, Arch. Dermat. & Syph. 59:36–44, 1949.

18. The Sign of Four, p. 93.

19. Southard, E. E.: Diagnosis per Exclusionem in Ordine: General and Psychiatric Remarks, J. Lab. & Clin. Med. 4:31–54, 1918.

20. Adventure of the Copper Beeches, p. 363.

21. Flügel, J. C.: The Psychology of Clothes, London, Hogart Press, 1930.

22. Code of Clothes.

Anal character: Love of orderliness—showing itself in exaggerated degree of cleanliness or neatness in manner of dress. Over-emphasis on possessions—buy new clothes but do not wear them, simply keep them for future and derive great pleasure in hoarding them. Dislike to throw out old clothing.

Obsessive compulsive men: Wear clean brown and white or black and white shoes.

Anxiety or anxiety hysteria: Loud colors, bright plaids, etc. Men wear loud, bright ties and shirts. Women often have immature hair styles.

Immature personality (female): "Little girl" hair styles (bangs, curls, shoulder-length hair in older women); not dressing "their age"—women over 30 trying to look in their teens or college age; bows or ribbons on hair; frills, bracelets; school rings and pins.

Immature personality (male): Older men in college clothes, "old school" ties; fraternity pins; argyle socks; loafers; moccasins, excessive use of sport clothes in a city dweller, etc.

Depressed (female): Excessive use of gray, pale or dark blue, drab browns and black. Women with dyed hair not caring enough about appearance to keep it dyed. Careless dress in a normally careful, fastidious woman.

Homosexual (female): Mannish hair style, copying male dress as nearly as possible, preference for rough, coarse materials.

Exhibitionist (female): Low necklines, dangling earrings, radical styles, ultramodern.

Homosexual (male): Aesthetic taste in clothes—fine materials, pastel shades—excess of yellow. Padded shoulders.

23. The Sign of Four, p. 97.

24. The Sign of Four, p. 91.

25. Klauder, J. V., and Robertson, H. F.: Symmetrical Serous Synovitis (Clutton's Joints), J. A. M. A. 103:236–240, 1934.

26. Klauder, J. V.: Ocular Syphilis: IV. Interstitial Keratitis and Trauma; Clinical, Experimental and Medicolegal Aspects, Arch. Ophth. 10:302–328, 1933.

27. Klauder, J. V.: Erysipeloid as an Occupational Disease, J. A. M. A. 111: 1345–1348, 1938.

28. The Adventure of the Blanched Soldier, p. 1188, the olfactory sense of Sherlock Holmes detected the curious tarry odor emanating from the brown leather gloves worn by Ralph, the butler.

29. A Case of Identity, p. 214.

30. A Case of Identity, p. 219.

31. Hyde, J. N.: A Practical Treatise on Disease of the Skin, Ed. 4, Philadelphia, Lea & Febiger, 1897.

32. This is quoted from Doyle, A. C.: Memories and Adventures, London, Hadden & Stoughton, 1924, p. 114. It was told to Doyle by the person who experienced the phenomenon. He writes that he had no reason to doubt the veracity of her experience. Discussion of similar phenomena is afforded by Klauder, J. V.: Stigmatization, Arch. Dermat. & Syph. 37:650–659, 1938.

33. Some former students of Dr. Udo Wile (Emeritus Professor of Dermatology, University of Michigan) informed me that in teaching dermatology he assigned reading of certain Sherlock Holmes' stories. Dr. Wile verified this (in a personal communication) and informed me that in teaching dermatology —class demonstrations, he employed the method of teaching herein described as the Sherlockian method.

It is to be recalled that in translation, the Sherlock Holmes' stories have been used as a textbook for the Egyptian police force, and the pre-Communist police force of China.

34. A Study in Scarlet, p. 13.

35. Klauder, J. V.: Pityriasis Rosea: A Clinical Study, Internat. Clin. 2:78–84, 1923; Pityriasis Rosea with Particular Reference to Its Unusual Manifestations, J. A. M. A. 82:178–183, 1924.

36. A Case of Identity, p. 219.

37. A Study in Scarlet, p. 6.

38. Klauder, J. V.: Actual Causes of Certain Occupational Dermatoses: A Study of 527 Cases, with Special Reference to Dermatoses Due to Mineral Oils, Arch. Dermat. & Syph. 48:579–600, 1943.

39. A Study in Scarlet, p. 13.

40. A Study in Scarlet, pp. 5 and 6.

41. For list of Sherlock Holmes' publications see: Roberts, S. C.: Dr. Watson, London, Faber & Faber, Ltd., 1931; Some Observations on Sherlock Holmes and Dr. Watson at Barts, St. Bartholomew's Journal, December, 1951. Catalogue, The Sherlock Holmes Exhibition presented by Adrian M. Conan Doyle, England, L. Middleditch Co., 1952. LaCour, T.: Ex Bibliotheca Holmesiana, Copenhagen, The Danish Baker Street Irregulars, 1951.

42. The Sign of Four, pp. 93 and 94.

43. The Red Headed League, p. 196.

44. Of the many structural abnormalities that have been attributed to congenital syphilis, apparently study of the ear has been neglected as a possible site of stigma of the disease. I (J. V. K.) therefore made photographs of the ears of children with congenital syphilis and compared them with similar photographs of nonsyphilitic children. Of the considerable variation in configuration of the ears of the two groups, no characteristic variation was apparent in the syphilitic group (unpublished study).

45. The Cardboard Box, p. 1053.

46. The adventure of the Blanched Soldier, p. 1192.

47. Sherlock Holmes purposely specified "in human beings" since the eruption of "diamond back" disease in swine comprises many unique, bizarre designs suggestive of dermatitis factitia, see Klauder, J. V.: Erysipelothrix Rhusiopathiae Infection in Swine and in Human Beings: Comparative Study of Cutaneous Lesions, Arch. Dermat. & Syph. 50:151–159, 1944.

48. A Scandal in Bohemia, p. 179.

49. A Case of Identity, p. 220.

50. Klauder, J. V., and Winkelman, N. W.: Pellagra Among Chronic Alcoholic Addicts, J. A. M. A. 90:364–371, 1928.

2

Gentlemen, the Queen

KENNETH MARK COLBY, M.D.

THOSE WHO PLAY CHESS are often reminded, happily or unhappily, of the Queen's might. Twice the strength of the next-ranking piece, the Queen has great mobility in moving in any straight direction, any chosen distance. Such a powerful scope makes her, of all the chessmen, the most welcomed ally and the most dreaded antagonist.

A cursory reflection on the psychology of this Amazonian state of affairs brings two questions readily to mind. First, what is a woman doing in an otherwise all-male combat, and, secondly, once present how is it that she is stronger by far than any of the men? From the standpoint of prevailing relationships between men and women in our phallocentric civilization, the structure of chess offers a startling turnabout.

Historical scholars of the game have little enough to contribute to our questions. It is known from the few facts available that the figure of the Queen in chess is entirely a European innovation introduced in the late 11th or early 12th century. Until that time chess, of Indo-Persian origin in the seventh century A.D., consisted wholly of male figures organized into rival armies and equipped as infantry, cavalry, and charioteers. Each army fought to capture the opposing king at whose side stood an advisor destined in later years to undergo a change in gender. In this form the game was brought to Europe by the invading Moors around 1000 A.D. The first chess manuscripts describing the Queen as replacing the king's advisor date from the 12th century. Why the king's minister was discarded in favor of the king's wife and who advocated this substitution is unknown.

One speculation regarding this modification has lingered in chess histories, though Murray (4), the leading English authority, dubs it a "pretty guess." Before the French Academy in 1719

Reprinted from THE PSYCHOANALYTIC REVIEW,
Volume 40, Pages 144–148, April 1953.

Freret proposed the Queen's entry as resulting from a linguistic confusion between *fierge* (French for the Arabian *firz*, advisor) and *vierge*, French for maiden. Psychoanalytic contributions are limited to Coriat's suggestion that the change was "probably motivated by the resemblance of chess to a family conflict" (2). Jones (3) only repeats Freret's idea. Along the lines indicated by Coriat one might add that the introduction of the king's wife into chess is a further example of man's repeated tendency to instill into his adult activities the childhood ingredients of the Oedipal situation. For clearly, on an elementary level of symbolism, the king stands for the father and the Queen for the mother. A cultural impetus for this Oedipal modification perhaps stemmed from the pervasive Christian imagery of that time which conceived of the Virgin as the Queen of Heaven and mother of the Holy Family.

The second of our two questions—the origin of the Queen's power—is also uncertainly answered by what historical facts are available. We know that when the king's advisor was altered to represent the Queen there was no accompanying change in the relative strength of the chesspiece, since it remained as before, weaker than the Rook and the Knight but slightly stronger than the Bishop. Not until the late 15th century did the Queen attain her presentday power. This comparatively sudden and spectacular promotion occurred between 1485 and 1500, probably in Italy, and resulted in the Queen becoming the strongest of all chesspieces, ten times more powerful than the Pawn and twice as strong as the Rook. With the increase in the attacking and defending powers of both chess armies, the game quickened, a consequence resented by the advocates of the old style of play who named the new game *alla rabiosa* (mad chess) and *esches de la dame enragee* (chess with the furious Queen). But the revolutionaires soon won out and by 1520 the old game was obsolete in European countries.

Here, too, we have no record of the whos and whys in this remarkable elevation of the Queen to supremacy. Other games of the time—cards, tables, merels, dice—escaped any such modification. The literature of chess, greater than that of all other games combined, is strangely silent on the question. Yet the very nature of the change, a woman being made the most powerful figure among warring men, offers data for a reasonable psycho-analytic reconstruction. Unfortunately for scientific precision but perhaps fortunately for the freely-associating speculator, the facts are too meagre to establish a verifiable hypothesis. So as in most historical sciences, the propositions and hypothesis that I shall state are in the nature of logical and psychological guesses about the man responsible for the Queen's new strength.

For I would first assume that it was a man and not a woman who changed the game. Indeed, it might be an attractive hypothesis to suppose that some vigorous lady, fiercely resentful of a masculine world's depreciation of her sex symbolized in one way by the Queen's lowly chess rank, might have expressed her protest in such a form. To her, the Queen's preeminence would help right the balance of an androcentric bias, at least in chess if little elsewhere. Actually a few aristocratic women of the 15th century did play chess as a pastime. But none of them gave it serious study, wrote manuscripts or was known to be influential in chess circles. True, a woman might have conceived of a stronger Queen and then impressed her idea on her husband who was active in the chess world. But here we have to postulate so many elements that a plausible hypothesis becomes over-stretched.

No, I believe a man empowered the Queen—a man well-known to a group or groups of serious chessplayers who initially would respectfully listen to and try out his innovation until it caught on lastingly by appealing to something in each one of them.

When an inventor or painter or musician creates something called "new," he assembles known and familiar elements into a uniquely different organizational pattern. Since this effort psy-chologically represents an attempt to solve important psycho-dynamic conflicts, the achieved Gestalt both formally and contextually expresses the nature of these conflicts. What can we say about psychology of our chess innovator? First, he enjoyed the repeated struggles that chess contests provide. Chess as a game is a play avenue for the discharge of impulses concerning fighting, attacking, hurting and killing. It provides for the sub-limation of pre-genital sadistic impulses and the mastery of anxiety connected with them. One fights with intent to demolish an opponent bent on doing the same (the words "check mate" are from the Arab Shah mat, meaning "the king is dead"). The weapons are ideas which clash via the tangible symbols of chess-pieces. This type of war-like activity was one personality need of the innovator. In raising the Queen's power he made chess more lively from an aggressive viewpoint, shortened the duration of each game and thus allowed the drama of the tension-resolution-tension cycles to be repeated more often in the playing time available. For some reason he had to quantitatively augment the sublimatory opportunities for his sadistic and aggressive impulses.

An even more specific formulation can be reached by examining the content of the innovation. In sum, it depicts an inter-personal situation in which a powerful and strapping female (Queen) fights for and protects a relatively helpless male (King) in hostile surroundings. I would think our man looked on himself as a weakling and, identifying himself with the weak King, elevated the Queen to superiority unconsciously as an expression of his instinctual wish to have a strong woman take care of him and to strive against an adverse world for him. In dynamic-genetic terms this desire represents an oral-dependent wish hark-ing from the first years of life when the infant's passive-receptivity gains gratification through a giant woman of seemingly unlimited power.

That such a wish-impulse was charged with sufficient energy to make such a radical impact on the innovator's chess thinking, leads me to propose further that it carried significant weight in his other psychological operations, particularly those involving women. For example, we could imagine that he repeatedly placed himself in a submissively subordinate position towards women, allowing them to rule over him and leaning greatly on their support. Had he been married, his chosen partner was of a dominant aggressive character, the personification of a chess Queen. In life, as in chess, he tended to relegate the sovereignty of a symbiosis to a particular type of woman.

Out of a man's ambivalent conflict between a desire to be allied with a powerful virago and a hatred of her domination as the badge of his weakness, the chess Queen was empowered. The changed game then represented a compromise formation in which both elements of this conflict gained expression.

What stirs in an individual stirs in his culture. That the inno-vation achieved quick popularity which persists until today, indicates that many others of that time and society found the new game alluring. At a period in history when people began to find a need for the sounding of quarter-hours on public clocks, the enlivened Queen accelerated chess play in keeping with this new cultural feeling about time. Nor was the concept of a powerful Queen in real life unusual to 15th century Europeans. Their literary heritage of Greco-Roman myths and history included many instances of strong women who ruled men. And during that century Isabella of Spain (1451–1504), Beatrice d'Este (1475–1497) and Lucrezia Borgia (1480–1523) were well-known examples. But the most fitting cultural model for the chess Queen was Caterina Sforza (1462–1509), "the warrior-countess of Forli" (1) who wore men's armor, carried a sword, led troops into battle on horseback and ruled—often cruelly—the Italian city-state of Romagna because her husband, the rightful king, was too weak to do it himself. Her personality and deeds were celebrated in many poems, ballads and plays and perhaps, as I would suggest, unconsciously in chess.

To determine how the idea of an individual becomes the fad of a small group and then swells into a widespread and lasting cultural institution, would be to trace the intricate and manifold mechanisms of a society's cohesiveness. Integral are the interaction of similar instinctual needs moulded by similar child-training patterns, in turn determined by the shared historical experiences of a people evolving a civilization. Exactly how these things work is not only beyond the scope of this presentation but beyond me. All I was curious about was the status of the Queen in chess.

BIBLIOGRAPHY

1. Collison-Morley, L. The Story of the Sforzas. New York: Dutton & Co., 1934.
2. Coriat, I. The Unconscious Motives of Interest in Chess. Psychoanal. Rev., 28; 30, 1941.
3. Jones, E. The Problem of Paul Morphy; A Contribution to the Psychoanalysis of Chess. Int. J. Psychoanal., 12; 1, 1931.
4. Murray, H. R. A History of Chess. Oxford: Clarendon Press, 1913.

3

A Cardiology Anomaly
Albert Abrams (1863 - 1924)

NATHAN FLAXMAN, M.D.

AT THE TURN into the twentieth century a small book of 170 pages on the diagnosis and treatment of the diseases of the heart was published (1). On the title page the author was listed as Albert Abrams, A.M., M.D. (Heidelberg), and F. R. M. S., Consulting Physician for Diseases of the Chest, Mount Zion and the French Hospitals, San Francisco.

Being particularly interested in all books on the heart, especially cardiac texts published since the first by De Senac (2), I found the work of Abrams profoundly interesting because of his later notoriety. Some of his apt remarks seem intriguing, for instance:

An unprincipled physician could reap a harvest, by putting in condition for re-examination many rejected applicants, diseased or otherwise, for life insurance (3).

In view of his later spurious fame, the statement seems all the more remarkable. However, Abrams was well acquainted with the cardiac literature, for he quoted Peacock (4) on rupture of the heart valves after sudden strain. Some of the sentences in Abrams book have the pure quality of medical aphorisms, as:

No fallacy in medicine has been more carefully nourished than the belief that a cardiac murmur is always indicative of heart disease (5).

The murmur of mitral obstruction is the only murmur which has a specific character (6).

Early evidence of Abrams' mechanical inclinations appeared in this book. He used chest x-rays, presented a modified stethoscope, a rod to measure the intensity of the heart tones, a pneumatic cabinet for lung gymnastics, and a stethophonometer. These were not entirely new as he had written articles on them pre-

Reprinted from BULLETIN OF THE HISTORY OF MEDICINE
Volume 27, pages 252–267, May–June, 1953.

viously. That he had cardiological insight may be surmised from this statement:

> Unfortunately the belief yet survives, that the demonstration of a cardiac murmur, is the signal for digitalis, notwithstanding compensation is present (7).

An important passage in this book suggests a clue to his personality:

> A few years ago I exhibited before the California State Medical Society a series of lantern slides illustrating cardiac lesions diagnosed by the aid of Roentgen Rays. Many of my auditors no doubt regarded my exhibit as manufactured evidence, whereas, others, less captious, were inclined to regard the demonstration as a joke (8).

The book itself is concise, to the point, up-to-date as of 1900, and easy to read. Except for his own articles, there is no bibliography. At the time it was published, Abrams lived at the southwest corner of Van Ness Avenue and California Street in San Francisco. This house was destroyed in the earthquake and fire of 1906. Previous to and after the publication of his *Diseases of the Heart,* he was a very frequent and constant contributor to medical literature.

Albert Abrams was about 36 years old at the time the book on the heart appeared in print. He may have looked back on a difficult climb to a small pinnacle of success in medicine. One could easily have said that here was a man to make his mark in medicine in the twentieth century. This he certainly did, not as an esteemed physician of renown, but, rather, as one who has been termed "the outstanding medical quack of all time (10)."

MAN AND DOCTOR

Born in San Francisco to Marcus and Rachel (Leavy) Abrams, even the date of his birth became a debatable issue later. In 1860-5, the period in which his birth fell, San Francisco possessed considerable polish, being already the world's wife, but she was just a little sensitive about having been, before that, the gold-miner's wife. San Francisco admitted the frontier, but she desired friendly recognition as a metropolis-in-the-making (9).

Abrams himself gave the date of his birth as December 8, 1862 or 1863, or 1864, in answer to questionnaires sent to him over the years by the *Directory* of the American Medical Association (10). The 1863 date has been accepted as the correct one. Little is known of his family, his childhood, and early education. He attended and graduated in medicine from the University of Heidelberg in 1882. From this fact alone one may assume that his family had sufficient means not only to send him by Union Pacific, the first transcontinental railroad completed in 1869, and by boat to Germany, but also to maintain him there.

Years later, a doctor who signed himself "M. D., Leipzig" stated that it was preposterous to assume that anyone could obtain an M. D. degree from a German University at the age of 19 years (10). However, Polk's *Medical and Surgical Register* of 1886 listed him as a Heidelberg graduate of 1882, and of Cooper Medical College in 1883. Records from the two institutions confirmed the dates (10). Just how long he attended Heidelberg before he was granted the degree was not known. The fact remains that Abrams graduated from Heidelberg at the earliest at which any man had taken a Doctor's degree at that university in 100 years. This in itself indicates a precocity that might have forecast his later achievements.

In a letter from Heidelberg, published in April, 1883, which was the first of a great many writings that seemed to flow from his facile pen, Abrams discussed the medical curriculum courses, and teachers at the institution (11). This raises the question of how he obtained the M. D. degree at Cooper, the predecessor of Stanford University Medical School, in 1883. For in his second article, he gave his address as Neue Fredrichs St., Berlin (12). In his third article the same address was given as of March, 1884 (13). His San Francisco address did not appear until the fourth article in June, 1884 (14). Most likely, he returned home in the summer of 1882 and attended Cooper during the 1882–3 session. Then he probably went abroad again, to Berlin, for postgraduate work during 1883–4.

Albert Abrams was a man of exceptional intelligence and productivity, dapper to the degree of wearing a toupee and a cropped beard, but vain with driving ambition (15). In the early years of practice he was handsome with black, curly hair cropped short, aquiline features, pince-nez glasses on a ribbon, and a Van Dyke beard. He quickly built up a large and well paying practice, taught, and wrote both medical works and fiction. He also served as physician to an orphanage, but Harris (15) stated that the children feared his rough and almost brutal handling. For the first 15 years, however, Abrams held the respect of his colleagues and the loyalty of Lane and Cooper Medical College (15). In 1882, Cooper, also known as the Medical College of the Pacific, was located at Webster and Sacramento Streets. The school had been founded by Dr. Levi C. Lane and named for his uncle, Dr. Elias S. Cooper. Abrams became the President of the Alumni Association in 1888, but more important was the fact that he held the rank of Professor of Pathology there from 1893 to 1898. The esteem in which he was held in those early years seems also attested by his election to the presidency of the San Francisco Medico-Chirurgical Society in 1893 and as Vice-President of the State Medical Society of California in 1894. In the late nineties, shortly before the appearance of the cardiac text, his eccentricities became generally known to his colleagues.

His Writings, 1883 to 1901

The little book on *Diseases of the Heart* seemed to mark a turn on the medical highway for him. Previous to this he was the author of numerous articles and books on a variety of subjects. There were case reports on carbon monoxide poisoning (14), floating kidney (16), azospermia (17), tetany (18), poisoning by chlorate of potash (19), pulmonary atelectasis as a cause of anemia (20), lung syphilis (21), gastroptosis and merycismus (22), gonorrheal endocarditis (23), facial hemiatrophy (24), brain tumor manifested by Jacksonian epilepsy with operation (25), and progressive pernicious anemia with malignant disease of the stomach (26). He also wrote on the prophylaxis of trichinosis (27), the pneumatic cabinet and its use in the treatment of pulmonary diseases (28), mistakes in diagnosis (29), on physiological pulmonary atelectasis (30), congelation (31), new methods of demonstrating tubercle bacilli in the sputum (32), neuroses of the lungs (33), and pneumotomy (34).

His outstanding contribution of the nineteenth century, however, was the demonstration of the value of the x-ray in cardiac diagnosis (35).

Prior to the appearance of his first book, Abrams published an 18 by 15½ inch card on a *Synopsis of Morbid Urine* (35). The

Manual of Clinical Diagnosis (37) appeared when he was 27 years old. In this he was listed as Pathologist to the City and County Hospital of San Francisco. A second edition of this manual was issued in 1891 and a third edition in 1894. It was dedicated to his esteemed friend, Dr. Joseph O. Hirschfelder, Professor of Clinical Medicine at Cooper. In the preface of this manual Abrams showed a degree of modesty that belied his later years: "I have gathered a posie of other men's flowers, and nothing but the thread that binds them is mine own."

Six years later the publication of his *Diseases of the Heart* enhanced his reputation over the country. A little later he contributed to volume 5 of *A System of Physiologic Therapeutics* edited by Dr. Solomon Solis-Cohen (38). Abrams wrote on prophylaxis, personal and civic hygiene, and care of the sick. Other contributors to the ten volume series, among the noted American, English, French, and German authors, were Joseph McFarland, Henry Leffman, and Wayne Babcock, all of Philadelphia.

The F. R. M. S., listed on the title page of *Diseases of ths Heart* by Abrams, later became a controversial issue. It was not present in his *Manual of Clinical Diagnosis* or in his listing as a contributor to *A System of Physiologic Therapeutics*. In 1922, when Abrams was defended vigorously, along with the F. R. M. S., by the writer, Upton Sinclair (39), the *Journal of the American Medical Association* stated there was no organization known as the Royal Medical Society of Great Britain.

In the same year that his book on the heart appeared, he had another small book set in print. This was entitled *Scattered Leaves from a Physician's Diary* (40), and contained 59 pages. It is difficult to decide whether it should be classed as fact or fiction, since the language is flowery, repetitious, and redundant. Perhaps it represented his alter ego. The diary was "dedicated to my wife (he married Jeanne Irma Roth of San Francisco on Thanksgiving Day, 1897) in whose company, during a tour of the world, these stories were written." Under Leaf I, "My First Patient," he stated, "Much to my sorrow, I soon learned that only the rich and influential physician could afford to diagnose an obscure disease and call it by its technical term."

A good example of the effusive tone, as compared to the plainer language of his book on the heart, appears on the first page of this so-called diary.

One day, (Abrams wrote) when the gastric vacuum was becoming pronounced, and when the coloration of my feelings was assuming a cerulean aspect,—.

On Leaf II, entitled "A Scientific Courtship," there is the first important clue to the method and type of quackery that Abrams adopted and adapted some 12 to 15 years later. Whether this material represents truth or fiction I have not been able to determine. The scientific courtship refers to a Dr. Edmond Laidy, a colleague and clever heart specialist (could Abrams have been referring to himself?), who "on the evening of his return to his home, . . . became interested in an article from the pen of a German investigator; the article was entitled 'How to Prognosticate Longevity by a Microscopical Examination of the Blood' by Dr. Carl Ruprecht."

The diary contains also such unrelated items as A Modern Aesculapius, A Mystery of the Latin Quarter, The Imagery of Love, The Euthanasia Club, A Study in Light and Shadow, A Martyr to His Profession, and The Professor of Bacteriology. There is no doubt that some, if not all of these were fictional phantasy, but where the truth leaves off and fancy takes over cannot be determined. Perhaps Abrams himself reached a point where he could not differentiate between them. To the demagogue, the ability to distinguish between true and false, ethical and unethical, moral and immoral, has disappeared into the shadows. Peculiarly enough, this very same diary of 1900 was reprinted between hard covers in 1923, with an added feature, illustrations by William Gropper (41). After all the denials made by Abrams of his unusual interest in monetary returns, one cannot help but feel that this was a direct attempt to cash in on his notoriety.

His Writings After 1900

A series of ten articles on the diseases of the lungs and pleura (42) appeared after the cardiac text was published. In the same year there was one on the portraiture of medical practice (43). His interest in physical diagnosis, a field in which he excelled, was considerable, if judged by the amount he wrote on the subject. This led him into studies of the reflexes, the background for the later controversial issues. His best work was done with the fluoroscope in discovering the heart (44), and lung (45) reflexes. These, the recession of the ventricles or the lightening of a small area of the lung following stimulation of the overlying skin, he would demonstrate with zeal and pride. He taught maneuvers for the elicitation of the pleural friction sound (46), wrote on inhibition of the heart as an aid in diagnosis (47), described a new physical sign in dislocation of the heart (48), discussed the Litten phenomenon (49), the tracheal traction test (50), incipient pulmonary tuberculosis (51), and aneurysms of the thoracic aorta (52).

Articles on a variety of other subjects, besides those on physical diagnosis and the reflexes, flowed steadily from his unceasing pen after 1900. These were on stethophonometry (53), the treatment of the heart in typhoid and other infectious diseases (54), nutrition in pulmonary diseases (55), bronchial phthisis (56), cardioptosis (57), the classification, diagnosis and treatment of tuberculosis (58, 59), cardiosphanchnic phenomenon (60), the vasomotor factor in the clinical measurement of blood pressure (61, 62), sphymography of the abdominal aorta (63), new clinical phenomena (64), podography (65), amyl nitrite in hemoptysis (66), inhibition of asthmatic paroxysm (67), autointoxication and indicanuria (68), pharmaco-diagnosis of cardiac diseases (69), treatment of exophthalmic goiter (70), duodenal intubation (71), diagnosis and treatment of diseases of the heart (72, 73), augmented blood pressure (74), and symptomatic atelectasis (75).

In addition, Abrams wrote four more books in the period between 1901 and 1911. The first, during that period of unusual productiveness, was one of 49 pages on the *Nervous Breakdown* (76). The second, on *The Blues (Splanchnic Neurasthenia)* (77) was of 240 pages, enlarged to 254 in the second, to 287 in the third edition, all in the short space of four years. The third book, one of 268 pages, was on *Man and His Poisons* (78). And the fourth book, a mammoth of 1039 pages on *Diagnostic Therapeutics* (79) appeared in 1910.

THE REFLEXES OF ABRAMS

Along with his interests in the various aspects of physical diagnosis, he began to write about the reflexes of the various organs. His first report was on the x-ray in the study of the heart reflex (44). Three years later he labeled it the "cardiac reflex of Abrams" (80). He did the same with the lung reflex (45), and this too acquired his name (81). Perhaps if he had stopped there, both eponyms might have persisted and still be taught to students of physical diagnosis. When he endeavoured to demonstrate by percussion the liver reflex (82, 83), a $\frac{1}{2}$ inch recession of the liver dullness evoked by stimulation of the overlying skin, his eccentricities, already known to his colleagues, seemed to become accentuated. He continued with the knee-jerk (84), the stomach (85), aortic (86), intestinal (87), vertebral concussional (88), and splenic reflexes (89), and added his name to some of these. After 1904 his ideas of nerve reflexes were syncretized with those of osteopathy, with the resultant extravagant claims made for his system of treatment in such diseases as angina pectoris and aneurysm (90) by means of percussing the spine.

HIS ELECTRICAL AND MECHANICAL INTEREST

While at Heidelberg, Abrams took an interest in electricity. Gramme's dynamo was but a few years old and the Edison incandescent lamp had been demonstrated only three years previously. In his article on "Some Uses For the Application of Electricity" (13) Abrams discussed electrobioscopy, electrization of the phrenic nerve as a remedy for asphyxia and syncope, faradopuncture, use of electrical sound to detect the presence and site of a metallic body in the tissues, use of electricity as a therapeutic agent in obstetrics and gynecology, the treatment of emesis and gastroectasia with electricity, and electrolysis, with a review of the current literature to that date. Even by present day standards, it is an excellent article.

A few years later his articles on the pneumatic cabinet (28) were considered conservative and unenthusiastic. His interests then turned to congelation (31) as an aid in diagnosis and treatment. And it was not surprising that he next turned to the use of the x-ray in cardiac (35) and pulmonary diagnoses (91), having demonstrated its value in 1897. As has been mentioned, he presented these and other electrical and mechanical aspects in the cardiac text.

In 1907 there first appeared, under his name, the announcement of a vibratory instrument for percussion (92), but he did not go into this fully until 1910 when his book on *Spondylotherapy* was published (93). The term was a neologic creation of Abrams, who stated that spondylotherapy concerned itself only with the excitation of the functional centers of the spinal cord. His disciples called it the science of evoking the reflexes of the body both to diagnose and cure diseases. Surprisingly enough, this book on *Spondylotherapy* went through six editions in eight years. In between, he wrote one on *Progressive Spondylotherapy* (94) and contributed articles on the subject to medical journals (95). And between 1912 and 1914, Abrams gave "clinical courses" on spondylotherapy in various parts of the countary at a $50.00 fee.

THE ELECTRONIC REACTIONS OF ABRAMS (96)

This interest in mechanics and electricity in medicine finally ended in his "Electronic Reactions." In 1916 he presented his *New Concepts in Diagnosis and Treatment; Physio-Clinical Medicine* (97). This he called "the practical application of the electronic theory in the interpretation and treatment of disease." At the same time he founded the *Journal of Electronic Medicine,* first issued in September of 1916, and he edited the first six volumes.

Vibration in diagnosis and sympathetic vibration as a corrective were the essentials of this new concept. The diagnostic technic consisted in placing a drop of the patient's blood in a box called a "dynamizer," containing a "jungle of wires," batteries and a rheostat. The "dynamizer" was provided with an electrode which was placed on the forehead of a healthy subject facing westward in a dim light. From areas of dulness elicited by percussion of the healthy subject's abdomen, Abrams attained the diagnosis of either disease or religion. If this sounded absurd, there was the therapeusis of sympathetic vibrations supplied from another box, the "oscilloclast." As adjuvants, vividly colored ointments, supposedly of a certain radioactivity, were smeared

over the patient's abdomen. Abrams presented his electronic
reactions in medical journals, and founded a quarterly, *Physio-
Clinical Medicine,* devoted to the electronic reactions and to his
visceral reflexes. His final medical article, on electrobiography
(98), appeared in the fall of 1921, just before he became a *cause
célèbre.*

The Abramsism Controversy

Until 1922 "spondylotherapy" and the "ERA" (Electronic Reactions of Abrams) (99) received little attention from organized
medicine. In that year, however, because of the many letters
on these subjects and about Abrams himself, the Bureau of Investigation of the American Medical Association, through its *Journal,*
opened fire on him and his methods of practice. It was admitted
that he was a member of his local medical society and that he
held, through that, fellowship in the Association; and that he
had written voluminously. When the first article appeared
Abrams was giving courses in San Francisco, beginning the first
of each month for four weeks, at an honorarium of $200.00.

When asked about "spondylotherapy" he said:

Despite the fury of tongue or the truculence of pen, the osteopath and
chiropractor are inspiring the confidence of the community with their systems.
Right or wrong in their theory, they are in the vulgar parlance, "delivering
the goods." Spondylotherapy was a product of necessity—the translation of
an ignored field of medicine from a chaotic to a scientific basis (100).

From the address of 2135 Sacramento Street, where he lived,
he edited and published *Physico-Clinical Medicine.* This adver-
tised, among other things:

Dr. Abrams electrodes for electronic diagnosis........$ 6.00
"   "   Biodynameter 36.00
"   "   Reflex Set 36.00
"   "   Electro-concusser 120.00

The "oscilloclast" was rented to all comers, M. D.'s and others,
at $200.00 or $250.00, according to whether AC or DC was
needed, plus a monthly payment of $5.00 for each machine. It
was not sold, only leased, with the definite understanding that
the machine was not to be opened by the lessee. After the
first article appeared in the *Journal of the American Medical*

Association, more letters poured in, some questioning everything about him and others commending and defending him as a genius. Among the latter was a long one from the author, Upton Sinclair (39), who, in his then latest book, had devoted a few pages of eulogy to Abrams.

> (Sinclair wrote): Dr. Abrams follows the policy of ignoring attacks on his work, taking the view that in the long run, the man who cures disease makes his way in the world in spite of all opposition. However, it is easy to see that he has been deeply hurt by this attack on his reputation.

This letter also stated that Abrams had taught his methods to 200 or 300 physicians, and that a great number of these using his "oscilloclast are enjoying incomes of from $1000 to $2000 per week."

"The average charge," Sinclair added, "is about $200.00 for a *guaranteed cure of such diseases as syphilis, tuberculosis, cancer, and sarcoma.*"

Until that time Abrams charged $10.00 for the examination of blood specimens sent to him, but afterwards he boosted it to $25.00, with all checks made payable to a trust fund he established for the purpose of founding a research institute. In further articles in 1922, the American Medical Association, through its *Journal,* turned its heavy guns on Abrams, his methods, and his disciples, and fired broadsides repeatedly. He withdrew from his local medical society and thus, indirectly, from the American Medical Association, but the "lessees of his oscilloclasts" included 217 physicians and 130 osteopaths, some of whom had as many as eight machines (101). The *Journal* continued to show the misdiagnoses and fallacies of these (102). Based on testimony in a court case and investigation by Milliken, the famous physicist, Orbison (103) recommended that "Abrams and his tribe have their state licenses taken away from them."

After Abrams consistently refused to submit himself or his methods to the scrutiny of qualified investigators, the *Scientific American* (104) conducted a one year investigation of ERA. In a series of 12 monthly articles, this independent magazine concluded: "At best it is an illusion; at worse it is a colossal fraud." The followers of Abrams were branded as "crude blatant advertising quacks, near-quacks and faddists with a sprinkling of men who, while they liked to be considered respectable, were essentially unscientific and invariably venal." Fishbein (105) went much further when he said that Abrams was a willing scapegoat for thinking horses, spiritualistic mediums, and hysterical malingerers.

Not only did Abrams advertise in the press, but he also had an electric sign at Trafalgar Square (15). "Even at this period of large wealth," for the Abrams Foundation took in in the neighborhood of two million dollars, "he remained mercenary, and it was not uncommon in the free clinics of San Francisco to see patients with incurable diseases, the remnants of his colored ointment (Abrams' paint) on their abdomens, left moneyless and hopeless after their electronic treatments" (15).

Defenders of Abrams contended that he was a genius, not a quack, who discovered a method, not an instrument; that he inherited, at an early age, a vast fortune from his father and decided to devote his talents and his life to medical research; that his inherited wealth was such that questions of expense were of no account; and, finally, not one cent of the money made on ERA went to him, but to his foundation for research.

At the height of this controversy, which became an international issue (106), Abrams contracted pneumonia and died on January 3, 1924. He left no dependents, for he outlived two wives, Jeanne Roth and his second wife, Blanche Schwabacher whom he had married on September 28, 1915; and there were no children. With his death the ERA became an issue of the past in the United States. The subject either provoked a smile or a shrug. However, in 1928, four years after his death, his fantastic hokum was deluding the credulous in England, Canada, and France (107). Harris (15) summed up Albert Abrams as "a tangental colleague possessing the boastfulness of Paracelsus, the self-deception of the alchemists, the alertness, tenacity and ruthlessness of the robber barons. . . . In the autumn of his life, his colleagues, viewing this prostitution of profession, thought him a clever, money-mad neuropath. But the observing neurologists, thinking of fixity of ideas, expanded ego and his colored salves, placed him among the mentally deranged."

PLACE OF THE CARDIAC TEXT

Ironically, the little book on *Diseases of the Heart*, which in itself might have set him apart with notable and noted cardiologists, became an anomaly because of his quackery. Abrams' book was the twentieth text on the heart alone published since the first by De Senac in 1749. It may be classed as the nineteenth of the 19th century or the first of the twentieth century (108). Much more amazing is the fact that it was only the second cardiac text written by an American, having been preceded in the United States by that of Austin Flint in 1859 (109). Many American editions of English, French, and German cardiac texts appeared in the nineteenth century. Those of Corvisart (1806), Bertin (1833), Andry (1846) and Paul (1884) were of French origin. Burns (1809) is considered the first English and Hope's (1832) the first complete book on heart diseases, Stokes (1854), Walshe (1862), Fothergill (1879), Balfour (1882), Bramwell (1884), Sansom (1892), Broadbent (1897), and Gibson (1898) all wrote English cardiac texts. The works of Bamberger (1857), Fraentzel (1892), and Rosenbach (1897) were of German origin.

One may perhaps conclude that, despite the unsavory later career and deplorable medical ending of its author, *Diseases of the Heart* by Albert Abrams, M. D. (Heidelberg) ranks a place among the early cardiac texts, especially American, if only as a cardiologic anomaly.

BIBLIOGRAPHY

1. Abrams, A.: *Diseases of the Heart, Their Diagnosis and Treatment,* Chicago, G. P. Engelhard Co., 1900.
2. De Senac, J. B.: Traité de la structure du cœur, de son action, et de ses maladies, Paris, Barbon, 1749.
3. Abrams (ref. 1), p. 7.
4. Flaxman, N.: Peacock and Congenital Heart Disease; Thomas Bevill Peacock (1812–1882), *Bull. Hist. Med.,* 7:1061, 1939.
5. Abrams (ref. 1), p. 30.
6. *Ibid.,* p. 33.
7. *Ibid.,* p. 69.
8. *Ibid.,* p. 63.
9. Altrocchi, J. C.: *The Spectacular San Franciscans,* New York, E. P. Dutton & Co., 1949, p. 138.
10. Albert Abrams, *J. A. M. A.,* 78:1072, 1922.
11. Abrams, A.: Medical Education in Germany, *Pacific M. & S. J.,* 25:505, 1882–3.

12. Abrams, A.: The Etiology of Infectious Diseases, *Pacific M. & S. J.*, 26:153 and 199, 1883–4.

13. Abrams, A.: Some Uses for the Application of Electricity, *Pacific M. & S. J.*, 26:387, 1883–4.

14. Abrams, A.: Poisoning by Carbon Monoxide, *Pacific M. & S. J.*, 26:532, 1883–4.

15. Harris, H.: *California's Medical Story*, Springfield, Ill., C. C Thomas, 1932, pp. 322–324.

16. Abrams, A.: Floating Kidney; a Case and a Cure, *Pacific M. & S. J.*, 27:97, 1884–5.

17. Abrams, A.: Azospermia; Its Relation to Male Sterility, *Pacific M. & S. J.*, 30:569, 1887.

18. Abrams, A.: A Preliminary Note on a Case of Tetany, *Occidental M. Times*, 4:14, 1890.

19. Abrams, A.: A Fatal Case of Poisoning by Chlorate of Potash, *Occidental M. Times*, 6:23, 1892.

20. Abrams, A.: Pulmonary Atelectasis as a Cause of Anemia, *Tr. M. Soc. Calif.*, 1892, p. 37; *Med. News*, 62:293, 1893; *Medicine*, 1:513, 1895.

21. Abrams, A.: Report of a Case of Lung Syphilis, with Autopsy, *Occidental M. Times*, 7:363, 1893.

22. Abrams, A.: A Case of Gastroptosis and Merycismus, with Voluntary Dislocation of the Stomach and Kidney, *Med. News*, 65:405, 1895.

23. Abrams, A.: Report of a Case of Gonorrheal Endocarditis, *New York M. J.*, 64:293, 1896.

24. Abrams, A.: Note of a Case of Facial Hemiatrophy, *New York M. J.*, 64:582, 1896.

25. Abrams, A. and Tait, D.: A Case of Brain Tumor Manifested as Jacksonian Epilepsy; Operation, *Occidental M. Times*, 10:372, 1896.

26. Abrams, A.: Progressive Pernicious Anemia and Malignant Disease of the Stomach, *Med. Rec.*, 57:718, 1900.

27. Abrams, A.: The Prophylaxis of Trichinosis, *Rep. Bd. Health of California*, 9:149, 1884.

28. Abrams, A.: The Pneumatic Cabinet and Its Use in the Treatment of Pulmonary Diseases, *Sacramento M. Times*, 2:407, 1888; also, Report of 163 Cases Treated with the Pneumatic Cabinet, *Pacific M. J.*, 34:513, 1891.

29. Abrams, A.: Mistakes in Diagnosis, *Occidental M. Times*, 7:57, 1893.

30. Abrams, A.: Observations on Physiological Pulmonary Atelectasis, *Tr. M. Soc. of Calif.*, 1894, p. 33; *Med. Rec.* 44:268, 1894.

31. (a) Abrams, A.: Investigations on Congelation in Diagnosis and Treatment, *Tr. M. Soc. of Calif.*, 1894, p. 37.

    (b) Abrams, A.: Circumscribed Tonic Muscular Contraction: Reference to Congelation as an Aid to Diagnosis, *Am. Med. & Surg. Bull.*, 8:1487, 1895.

32. Abrams, A.: New Methods of Demonstrating Tubercle Bacilli in the Sputum, *Occidental M. Times*, 10:74, 1896.

33. Abrams, A.: A Contribution to the Study of Heretofore Undescribed Neuroses of the Lungs, *Tr. M. Soc., Calif.,* 1896, p. 116; *New York M. J.,* 63:767, 1896.

34. Tait, D. and Abrams, A.: Pneumotomy, *Med. News,* 72:263, 1898.

35. Abrams, A.: The Value of the Röntgen Rays in Cardiac Diagnosis, *New York M. J.,* 65:785, 1897.

36. Abrams, A.: *A Synopsis of Morbid Urine,* San Francisco, W. S. Duncombe, 1896.

37. Abrams, A.: *Manual of Clinical Diagnosis,* San Francisco, The Bancroft Co., 1891.

38. *A System of Physiologic Therapeutics,* edited by Dr. Solomon Solis-Cohen, Philadelphia, P. Blakiston's Son & Co., 1903.

39. Albert Abrams, A Defense by Upton Sinclair, *J. A. M. A.,* 78:1334, 1922.

40. Abrams, A.: *Scattered Leaves from a Physician's Diary,* St. Louis, Fortnightly Press, 1900.

41. Abrams, A.: *Diary of a Physician,* New York, Modern Press Corp., 1923.

42. Abrams, A.: Diseases of the Lungs and Pleura, *Med. Fortnightly,* 18:565, 639, 1900; 19:18, 203, 1901; 21:20, 49, 272, 307, 466, and 646, 1902.

43. Abrams, A.: Portraiture of Medical Practice, *Am. Therapist,* 8:129, 1900.

44. Abrams, A.: The X-Rays in the Study of the Heart Reflex, *Phila. M. J.,* 5:66, 1900; The Clinical Value of the Heart Reflex, *Med. Rec.,* 59:10, 1901.

45. Abrams, A.: The Lung Reflex, *New York M. J.,* 71:57, 1900.

46. Abrams, A.: The Pleural Friction-Sound: Maneuvers for its Elicitation, *Phila. M. J.,* 65:410, 1900.

47. Abrams, A.: Inhibition of the Heart as an Aid in Diagnosis, *Pacific M. J.,* 43:342, 1900; also *Phil. M. J.,* 6:601, 1900.

48. Abrams, A.: A New Physical Sign in Dislocation of the Heart, *Med. Rec.,* 58:372, 1900.

49. Abrams, A.: A Contribution to the Study of the Intercostal Phonation Phenomenon and the Litten Diaphragm Phenomenon, *Med. Rec.,* 64: 212, 1903.

50. Abrams, A.: The Tracheal Traction Test, *Med. News,* 84:1207, 1904.

51. Abrams, A.: The Physical Signs of Incipient Pulmonary Tuberculosis, *Med. Rec.,* 73:309, 1908.

52. Abrams, A.: Aneurysm of the Thoracic Aorta, *Med. Rec.,* 76:6, 1909.

53. Abrams, A.: Stethophonometry, *New York M. J.,* 72:265, 1901.

54. Abrams, A.: The Treatment of the Heart in Typhoid Fever and Other Infectious Diseases, *Med. News,* 78:410, 1901.

55. Abrams, A.: Nutrition in Pulmonary Tuberculosis, *J. Tuberc.,* 4:129, 1902.

56. Abrams, A.: Bronchial Phthisis, *New York M. J.,* 77:15, 1902.

57. Abrams, A.: Cardioptosis, *Med. News,* 83:337, 1903.

58. Abrams, A.: The Classification and Diagnosis of Pulmonary Tuberculosis, *Colorado M. J.,* 10:147, 1904.

59. Abrams, A.: The Treatment of Pulmonary Tuberculosis, *Medicine,* 10: 731-1904.

60. Abrams, A.: The Cardiosplanchnic Phenomenon, *Am. J. M. Sc.*, 127:125, 1904.
61. Abrams, A.: The Vasomotor Factor in the Clinical Measurement of the Blood Pressure, *Am. J. M. Sc.*, 127:910, 1904.
62. Abrams, A.: A Clinical Method of Determining the Vasomotor Factor in Blood Pressure, *Am. Med.*, 7:850, 1904.
63. Abrams, A.: Sphymography of the Abdominal Aorta, *Am. Med.*, 8:996, 1904.
64. Abrams, A.: New Clinical Phenomena, *Medicine*, 11:598, 1905.
65. Abrams, A.: Podography, *Am. Med.*, 10:561, 1905.
66. Abrams, A.: Amyl Nitrite in Hemoptysis, *Lancet*, 2:1685, 1906; 1:117, 1907.
67. Abrams, A.: Inhibition of the Asthmatic Paroxysm, *Med. Fortnightly*, 30: 611, 1906.
68. Abrams, A.: Autointoxication and Indicanuria, *Med. Rec.*, 73:689, 1908.
69. Abrams, A.: Pharmaco-diagnosis of Cardiac Diseases, *Arch. Diagn.*, 3:313, 1910.
70. Abrams, A.: Treatment of Exophthalmic Goitre, *Internat. Clin.*, 4:35, 1912.
71. Abrams, A. and Jarvis, G. D.: A New Method of Duodenal Intubation, *Arch. Diagn.*, 5:329, 1912.
72. Abrams, A.: Diagnosis of Diseases of the Heart, *Internat. Clin.*, 2:63, 1913.
73. Abrams, A.: Treatment of Diseases of the Heart, *Internat. Clin.*, 3:108, 1913.
74. Abrams, A.: Augmented Blood Pressure, *Internat. Clin.*, 4:49, 1913.
75. Abrams, A.: Symptomatic Atelectasis, *Med. Rec.* 93:276, 1918.
76. Abrams, A.: *Nervous Breakdown*, San Francisco, The Hicks-Judd Co., 1901.
77. Abrams, A.: *The Blues (Splanchnic Neurasthenia)*, New York, E. B. Treat & Co., 1904.
78. Abrams, A.: *Man and His Poisons*, New York, E. B. Treat & Co., 1906.
79. Abrams, A.: *Diagnostic Therapeutics*, New York, Rebman Co., 1910.
80. Abrams, A.: The Cardiac Reflex of Abrams, *Lancet*, 2:1052, 1903; The Heart Reflex and the Mechanism of Angina Pectoris, *Med. Rec.*, 72: 969, 1907; Percussion du cœur et détermination du ton du myocarde, *Presse méd.*, 18:938, 1910.
81. Abrams, A.: The Lung Reflex of Abrams, *Lancet*, 2:1756, 1903, Les Réflexes cardiaque et pulmonaire, *Presse méd.*, 15:209, 1907; Asthma and the Lung Reflexes of Abrams, *Med. Rec.*, 78:813, 1910.
82. Abrams, A.: Percussion of the Lower Border of the Liver, *Med. News*, 80:258, 1902.
83. Abrams, A.: The Liver Reflex, *Occidental M. Times*, 17:332, 1903.
84. Abrams, A.: The Knee-jerk, *Am. Med.*, 6:852, 1903.
85. Abrams, A.: The Stomach Reflex and Percussion of the Stomach, *Med. Rec.*, 66:377, 1904; The Vagovisceral Reflexes with Special References to the Vago Stomach Reflex, *Am. Med.*, 10:575, 1905; Clinical Physiology of the Stomach, *Am. J. Physiol. & Therap.*, 1:273, 1910–11.

86. Abrams, A.: The Aortic Reflex, *Am. Med.,* 7:542, 1904; The Aortic Reflexes, *Med. Rec.,* 68:459, 1905.
87. Abrams, A.: The Intestinal and Stomach Reflexes, *Medicine,* 10:44, 1904; Cardio-splanchnic Phenomenon of Abrams, *Brit. M. J.,* 1:1348, 1911; The Tonus of the Vagus, *Internat. Clin.,* 3:17, 1912.
88. Abrams, A.: The Vertebral Concussional Reflexes, *Am. Med.,* 9:640, 1905.
89. Abrams, A.: Splenic Reflexes of Abrams, *Med., Rec.,* 92:586, 1917; Splenic Reflexes of Abrams in Treatment of Syphilis, *Med. Rec.,* 95:96, 1919.
90. Abrams, A.: Contribution au traitement des anévrismes aortiques, *Presse méd.,* 19:785, 1911; The Treatment of Aortic Aneurysms, *Brit. M. J.,* 2:70, 1911; The Treatment of Aneurisms, *Internat. Clin.,* 4:23 and 51, 1913; Abrams' Method of Treatment in Aneurysms, *Med. Rec.,* 86:549, 1914.
91. Abrams, A.: Roentgen Rays in Pulmonary Disease, *J. A. M. A.,* 38:1142, 1902; Some Cardiorespiratory Phenomena Revealed by the Röntgen Rays, *Am. Med.,* 5:11, 1903.
92. Abrams, A.: Le vibro-suppressor; un nouvel instrument pour la percussion topographique, *Presse méd.,* 15:83, 1907.
93. Abrams, A.: *Spondylotherapy,* San Francisco, Philopolis Press, 1912, 3rd edition.
94. Abrams, A.: *Progressive Spondylotherapy,* San Francisco, Philopolis Press, 1913.
95. Abrams, A.: Principles and Practice of Spondylotherapy, *Internat. Clin.,* 2:14, 1912; Some New Things in Spondylotherapy, *Month. Cycl. & M. Bull.,* 6:393, 1913; Spondylotherapy, *Ref. Handb., Med. Sc.,* 7:910, 1917.
96. Abrams, A.: Electronic Reactions of Abrams, *Internat. Clin.,* 1:93, 1917.
97. Abrams, A.: *New Concepts in Diagnosis and Treatment; Physio-clinical Medicine,* San Francisco, Philopolis Press, 1916.
98. Abrams. A.: Electrobiography, *Med. Rec.,* 100:761, 1921.
99. Abrams, A.: ERA, *Med. Rec.,* 97:565, 1920.
100. "Spondylotherapy," *J. A. M. A.,* 78:913, 1922.
101. Abrams' "Oscilloclast," Some Lessees of this Therapeutic Device, *J. A. M. A.,* 79:1626, 1922.
102. Two Electronic Diagnoses, Reactions of Guinea-Pig and Sheep to Reaction of Abrams, *J. A. M. A.,* 79:2247, 1922; Another Electronic Diagnosis and Treatment; "Everything Clears Up"—But the Patient Dies, *J. A. M. A.,* 81:317, 1923; Two More Electronic Diagnoses, Findings Made by an Osteopath and a Physician, *J. A. M. A.,* 81:493, 1923.
103. Orbison, T. J.: Certain Electrical Diagnostic and Therapeutic Methods from Standpoint of a Neuropsychiatrist, *J. A. M. A.,* 81:2057, 1923.
104. Scientific American on Abrams "Electronic Reactions," *J. A. M. A.,* 83:939, 1924.
105. Fishbein, M.: Did Dr. Abrams Make a Real Discovery? *Forum,* 74:204, 1925.

106. Clark, O.: Abrams Method of Percussion and Spondylotherapy, *Brazil Med.*, 34:461, 1920; Barr, J.: Abrams Method of Percussion, *Lancet*, 1:1109, 1920; Horder, J.: Medicine and Old Ethicks, With Special Reference to Electronic Reactions, *Brit. M. J.*, 1:485, 1924; Humphris, F. H.: Exposure of ERA, *Lancet*, 1:176, 1924; ERA, *Brit. M. J.*, 1:179, 1925; van Rijnberk, G.: Annals of Human Credulity; Abrams' Electronic Reaction, *Nederl. Tijdschr. v. Geneesk,* 1:846 and 2:570, 1925.

107. Abramism Abroad, *J. A. M. A.*, 90:401, 1928

108. *See* Additional Bibliography.

109. Flint, A.: *Diseases of the Heart*, Philadelphia, Blanchard & Lea, 1859.

(An additional bibliography is listed in the original paper.)

4

The Human Side of Science

OTTO GLASSER, Ph.D.

Almost 60 years have passed since Wilhelm Conrad Röntgen, professor of physics at the University of Würzburg (in November 1895), saw the effect of a strange and unusual phenomenon while he was performing some experiments in his laboratory. This was the bright fluorescence of some barium platinocyanide crystals near an electrically excited Hittorf-Crookes tube. He pursued the study of this effect in a most masterly and thorough manner, and discovered it to be due to "new kind of rays," which he called the "x-rays" and which now are often called the "roentgen rays." This famous discovery, which so profoundly influenced many branches of science and medicine, placed Röntgen in the ranks of the world's great men.

With a discovery so epoch-making as that of the x-rays, and in view of the immediate and unprecedented interest in it on the part of the scientific world and the general public, it was perhaps inevitable that some confusions and even unjust criticisms concerning it should arise to disturb and plague Röntgen. Because he reacted to criticism with great sensitivity, and even bitterness —though he also did his best to avoid and evade acclaim—an account of these negative unpleasant accompaniments of the discovery forms an interesting chapter on scientific controversy and polemics.

Some of the controversy regarding priority in regard to certain phases or features of the discovery was undoubtedly not inspired by dishonesty, but rather by the confusion which arose naturally from the tremendous publicity concerning the new scientific wonder and ignorance concerning its real nature. The distinction between the new rays and the well-known cathode rays was confusing to nonscientific minds, and this confusion was evident in some of the stories that were circulated regarding the discovery.

Reprinted from Cleveland Clinic Quarterly
Volume 20, pages 400–405, July, 1953.

Another factor which gave rise to some of the unfounded and inaccurate accounts of the event was the desire of certain little persons in the periphery of Röntgen's environment to gain personal prestige by pretending to know some "inside story" connected with it. These gossipy rumors and descriptions undoubtedly were exaggerated and magnified by Röntgen's aversion to publicity and his own reticence in discussing the actual happenings.

In addition to these factors, it is unpleasant to record that evidently most of the unfair criticism came from certain scientists who were jealous of Röntgen's success. Many prominent scientists had been investigating the cathode rays, and felt chagrin that they had failed to observe the phenomena which led Röntgen to detect the existence of the x-rays, although undoubtedly x-rays had been produced in their experiments, as was recognized after the discovery was announced.

False claims of priority and attempts to belittle the importance of the discovery and Röntgen's genius in making it were already appearing early in 1896, even before the first tumult of acclaim and praise had subsided. Although these criticisms were puzzling and disturbing to Röntgen, he apparently resolved to ignore them philosophically, as he indicated in a letter to his friend Ludwig Zehnder: "My work has received recognition from many quarters . . . This is worth a great deal to me, and I let the envious chatter in peace; I am not concerned about that." Nevertheless, the record and his own behavior later clearly demonstrate that he was concerned about it, and became increasingly so with the passage of the years. He mentioned it in letters to his friends only a year or so before his death. As his resentment increased, his reticence became more and more pronounced, and reached such exaggerated proportions that, after his three original communications, he refused to publish anything more on the x-rays; and he also stipulated in his will that all records of his work and all correspondence about the discovery between 1895 and 1900 be burned unopened at his death—a provision, which, unfortunately for the historical record, had to be carried out.

The claims of priority in the discovery arose largely from confusion regarding the reports of previously unexplained accidents caused by the x-rays. Sir William Crookes, whose cathode-ray

tubes Röntgen had used in many of his experiments, had observed
that unopened boxes of photographic plates were fogged and
had complained repeatedly to the manufacturer that they were
unsatisfactory. That this effect was caused by x-rays he did not
know until their discovery was announced. Others had had similar experiences with photographic plates, but had not investi-
gated the reason for it. A. W. Goodspeed, professor of physics at
the University of Pennsylvania in Philadelphia, actually made
an accidental x-ray photograph on February 22, 1890, during
the process of demonstrating a Crookes' tube. He kept it with a
collection of freak photographs, but recalled and unearthed it
six years later, when the discovery of x-rays was announced, and
proved that it was actually an x-ray photograph. Goodspeed
described this in a lecture on the roentgen rays which he gave
in February 1896 but added: "We can claim no merit for the
discovery, for no discovery was made."

Typical of the inaccurate descriptions and stories about the
discovery was the fable of book and key, which was originated by
an American student attending Würzburg University and widely
circulated in the United States. This gave April 30, 1895, as the
date. "Röntgen had a Hittorf tube covered by a light tight paper
energized by a coil and was studying the fluorescence of the
screen one afternoon, and being called away for a few minutes,
he laid the glowing tube upon a book which contained a large
flat key, which was being used for a bookmark. A loaded photographic plateholder happened to be lying under the book.
When he returned he shut off the current from the tube, took
the plate holder with several others and spent the afternoon out
of doors, exposing several plates in the practice of his favorite
hobby, photography. On developing the plates, he found the
shadow of the key bookmark on one of them. He wondered how
this happened and questioned several of the students, but none
could explain the incident."

This story has had wide appeal for the general public, and
has reappeared in numerous distorted versions of the discovery,
but even in its original form, it contains inaccuracies. Laying a
glowing tube on a book would necessitate disconnecting the
high voltage from the tube and hence no x-rays could be
produced. "Studying the fluorescence of the screen" around a

Hittorf tube would indicate that the fluorescent effect of the rays had been noticed previously. Neither Röntgen nor any of his intimate colleagues and friends ever spoke of anything connected with the book and key experiment. Röntgen was always most accurate and painstaking in recording experimental data, yet he never referred to any such observation on April 30, 1895. His two senior assistants, one of whom helped to evacuate the Hittorf tubes, did not know about the discovery of the x-rays until Röntgen's announcement in December 1895. If these men who were working rather intimately with Röntgen knew nothing of the discovery, it seems extremely unlikely that a student at the University should have had any inside information as to the work the professor was doing.

One of the most pernicious and persistent rumors was that the discovery was merely an accident and that the first crucial observation of the fluorescence of the screen was made by a laboratory assistant. In his last years, Röntgen once said, "What miserable envious soul must have invented this story."

Of all the criticism and antagonism directed towards Röntgen, the most distressing to him was the attitude of Philipp Lenard, which grew increasingly bitter and puzzling with the years, and continued—so far as Lenard was concerned—after Röntgen's death in 1923.

Of the scientific events antedating the discovery of the x-rays, Lenard's scientific contributions on the properties of the cathode rays immediately preceded and undoubtedly were a principal factor in stimulating Röntgen's researches that led to recognition of the "new" rays. However, Lenard's work and also Röntgen's, rested on the discoveries of many scientific predecessors, especially the experimental work of Hertz—who was Lenard's teacher— and the theories of von Helmholtz. Röntgen gave Lenard due credit for his "wonderful" experiments in his first communication and also mentioned the Lenard vacuum tube as one of those he used in his experimental work. Immediately after the discovery, Lenard's attitude toward Röntgen was friendly, as proved by letters still in existence, but a definite antipathy and bitterness, on Lenard's part, appeared at about the time Röntgen received the first Nobel prize for physics in 1901. From the time when Lenard himself received the Nobel prize in 1905, it seemed clear that he had embarked upon a campaign to minimize the work of Röntgen, and to make him appear a bungler who merely happened accidentally to make a great discovery. He said in his Nobel prize lecture: "In reality I had made several unexplainable observations which I carefully kept for future investigation—unfortunately not started in time—which must have been the effects of traces of wave radiation." In his publications on cathode rays which appeared before Röntgen's discovery, Lenard did not mention these observations: hence any attempt to give Lenard the credit for discovery of the x-rays is without any historical foundation.

In Lenard's publications during later years, he has either ignored Röntgen or dismissed him and the x-rays (high-frequency rays, as he called them) in a casual footnote. He has tried to perpetuate the idea that anyone who was wide-awake and using a Lenard tube could have discovered the x-rays. He excuses his own failure to discover them by saying that, as a good scientist, he concentrated on his own special line of investigation and postponed the study of strange phenomena until after his original work was completed.

During a controversy in 1929, Lenard intimated that perhaps more data in regard to the discovery of "high-frequency rays" might be revealed at a later date. On August 18, 1929, he wrote to me: "There is no doubt that the road to the discovery led over my researches. At that time I was prevented by external circumstances from pursuing to my satisfaction in every direction the great number of new phenomena that appeared in my studies on cathode rays. But in my opinion, this is not yet the proper time to express myself more thoroughly on the subject than I did in my Nobel prize lecture. That would be only biographical anyway, and what has already been said must suffice for the judicious. With this I believe that I have done everything that the history of science can expect of me on this point at this particular time." Lenard continued later to maintain this enigmatic attitude.

It is interesting that Lenard's extreme nationalism and strong anti-Semitic prejudice assured him an outstanding position in Hitler's regime, and added great weight to whatever he had to say. Hence, with the ascendency of the Nazis, the controversy regarding the credit that Lenard should receive in connection with the discovery of the x-rays assumed distorted and exaggerated proportions that extended outside the realm of a priority claim in the field of physics. In 1935, friends of Lenard made a concerted effort to prove that Röntgen used the Lenard tube in making the discovery, but the evidence was not sufficient to alter the story of the discovery. Just preceding and during the war years, there was considerable discussion, carried out with the help of the Nazi press and some party members, over the position of Röntgen in the annals of science. Articles appeared in certain daily papers suggesting that he had done nothing remarkable, but merely had carried to its inevitable conclusion the work of the great Aryan scientist, Philipp Lenard, Director of the Physical Institute at Heidelberg University.

In 1944, the Physical-Medical Society of Würzburg made application to the Nazi Minister of Post and Telegraph to have a memorial stamp made for Röntgen, marking the fiftieth anniversary of the discovery of the x-rays, similar to the one issued for Robert Koch and other scientists; but the request was rejected with the comment that the proposal was not in order inasmuch as such an honor was reserved only for the illustrious. The Minister of Post, Dr. Ohnesorge, happened to be a good friend of Lenard's. Seven years later, the Ministry of Post of the Federal Republic of Western Germany issued a Röntgen-stamp at the occasion of the fiftieth anniversary of the award of the first Nobel prize in physics to Röntgen (fig. 1).

In Lenard's four volume work, "Deutsche Physik," there is no mention of Röntgen or of Einstein in the text, and the foreword is a diatribe against the Jews. Many persons in Hitler's Germany naturally drew the inference that Röntgen was a Jew. When Lenard was asked directly, "Was Röntgen a Jew?" he replied, "No, but he was a friend of Jews and acted like one."

That Röntgen had good Jewish friends is a fact, for he mentioned them frequently, and with affection, in his letters. It is also true that he condemned anti-Jewish prejudice, as shown in this letter to a friend, written May 12, 1921: "The anti-Semitic incidents in Würzburg of which you write are exceedingly regrettable; it is not much better here (Munich). For instance, there is scarcely an advertisement of rooms for University students which does not contain the statement, 'No Jews,' and I know of one instance when a woman said to a student who was looking at a room and mentioned his name, which sounded Jewish, 'I do not take any Israelites.' It is a bad sign of the times that decent persons can thus be so rudely insulted."

Fig. 1. Röntgen-stamp issued in 1951 by the Ministry of Post of the Federal Republic of Western Germany at the occasion of the fiftieth anniversary of the award of the first Nobel prize in physics to Röntgen.

The record shows that Lenard's animosity towards Röntgen's —which would seem to be based on resentment of Röntgen's greater fame—became more intense with the years. The extreme bitterness in his old age (83 years in 1945) was expressed in an interview with Lewis Etter as follows: "I am the mother of the

-rays. Just as a midwife is not responsible for the mechanism
f birth, so was Röntgen not responsible for the discovery of the
-rays, which merely fell into his lap. All Röntgen had to do was
ush a button, since all the groundwork had been prepared by
ne . . . Without my help the discovery of x-rays would not have
een possible even today. Without me the name Röntgen would
e unknown. Röntgen was an opportunist who sensed that there
as something to be found in experimenting with my tube
which he carried out with an eye to fame . . . I was always too
modest and did not rush into print. In my letter to Röntgen
where I praised him for his great discovery I thought he would
eply that he really owed it all to me and my tube, but I waited
or this acknowledgement from him in vain."

It is sad and disillusioning that a man like Lenard, whose
scientific achievements rank with the best, should be so consumed by jealousy that he should also try to take credit for the
great discovery of a fellow scientist. It is also disappointing that
one trained in the scientific method should forsake the broad,
impartial, honest integrity—the ideal of Truth—of the scientific
viewpoint and degrade himself by expressions of narrow partisan-
ship, racial prejudice and petty jealousy and slander. This indicates that some scientists—though fortunately they are few in
number—fail to live up to the high ideals of the cause they serve.

It was precisely because he failed to measure up to the high
ideal of truth, which is the essence of science, that Lenard found
such high favor in the Nazi regime. He tried to add to his own
renown by subtracting from Röntgen's glory, and he succeeded
temporarily, in his own country, because the environment of the
Third Reich was one in which prejudice flourished.

When seen against this distorted background, the character of
Röntgen stands out in bold relief. Because he was a man of real
integrity—the true scientist in his life as in his work—and hence
could not tolerate intolerance, his memory was not revered by
the National Socialists. That they could not regard him as illustrious is, in one sense, a measure of his true universality and
greatness. In democratic Germany and elsewhere in the world,
Röntgen's honor and fame have steadily increased during the
almost 60 years that have elapsed since his great discovery.

BIBLIOGRAPHY

Etter, L. E.: Some historical data relating to discovery of roentgen rays. Am. J. Roentgenol. 56:220–231 (Aug.) 1946.

Glasser, Otto: Genealogy of roentgen rays. Am. J. Roentgenol. 30:180 (Aug.) 1933, 30:349 (Sept.) 1933.

Glasser, Otto: Wilhelm Conrad Röntgen and the Early History of the Roentgen Rays. Springfield, Illinois, Thomas, 1934, p. 494.

Glasser, Otto: Dr. W. C. Röntgen. Springfield, Illinois, Thomas, 1945, p. 169.

Glasser, Otto: Strange repercussions of Röntgen's discovery of x-rays. Radiology 45:425–427 (Nov.) 1945.

Zehnder, L. W. C.: Röntgen, Briefe an L. Zehnder. Zurich, Rascher, 1935.

LOOKING BACKWARD

—————— 5 ——————

Medicine and the Bible

LOUIS A. M. KRAUSE, M.D.

SOMEONE TOLD ME a while ago that it took a lot of nerve or courage to talk about the Bible. I feel, however, that it is a safe subject. Most of you know little or nothing about the Bible, and if something were wrong, I doubt if you would recognize the error. That is probably true for the Hebrews as well as the Christians who are present.

I have been interested in the pathology of the ancients for years. What we are actually trying to do, is to reconstruct the course of diseases over the ages, from several points of view.

There is one thing to remember when interpreting literature; always put yourself in the framework of the time in which the story is written. Then, I think you will be less critical, more humble, and not make the mistake of underestimating the intelligence of the ancients.

After we have studied the literary remains, we go out into the area and dig. An endless amount of pathology has been found in the graveyards of Egypt. The bodies found are well preserved, from the point of view of the bony structures, the skin, and many times the internal organs.

We can re-hydrate the tissues rather well, so that microscopic sections of them can be made which don't look too unlike a specimen; a slide prepared three, four, five or ten years ago, the stain will be a little weak or faint, but the morphology can be determined.

Now, bear in mind that we are also interested in other things.

Presented at the 142nd Annual Meeting of the Rhode Island Medical Society, at Providence, R. I., May 6, 1953.

We are also trying to study the cultural and social fabric of the peoples who are mentioned in the Bible. By studying their social and cultural fabric we are able to determine how they handled their sick and their dead. There isn't a single force greater than the impulse of human affection.

I am sure all of us stand on the foundation of the Judeo-Christian ethics, and that is the reason I believe we can learn much from the people who are responsible for our Bible. They have given us so much, and yet we have hardly approached the ideal or pattern set before us by the ancient prophets, who reached their zenith in the New Testament.

Another important thing to remember when you are interpreting various passages, is what the ancients believed: that disease sooner or later followed sin. However, today we look for the fundamental processes behind the scenes. No medical school teaches that disease is the result of sin.

If you assume that disease follows sin, then your next premise, of necessity, would be to offer a sacrifice or an appeasement to the angry god.

That is exactly what the ancients did. In the case of tuberculosis, pneumonia, ulcer or tumor, the ancients did not seek a natural cause. They sought the priest. In this way they hoped either to be cured or protected from the malady, whatever the case might be. Surprising as it may seem, this belief lasted well into modern times. And, it was the confusion of magic and religion with healing that helped retard medical progress for years.

Our gross pathology is quite abundant in our findings. We have seen a great deal of evidence of diseases of the bones, as tumors, malignant and otherwise. We have also seen a great deal of evidence of diseases of the skin.

Incidentally, since the word leprosy has been used to designate the disease in Leviticus XIII and XIV, much confusion has been caused. The confusion has been brought about by the Latin word *lepra* because it was originally used in two distinct senses. When the word lepra was used to denote a mere skin disease it was synonymous with the Greek *lepro,* the meaning of which is rough or scaly. The Old Greek version of the Pentateuch translates the Hebrew *tsara ath* by *lepro* of the Greek medicine.

Now probably you can understand why the leprosy of the Bible, is not the disease we know as leprosy today. We never see a leper who has a lesion that is "white as snow."

A mummy has been found who died at the height of his smallpox, with the confluent vesicles, and all other changes you may be familiar with, if you have seen smallpox in the living today.

We have repeatedly found bladder stone, and probably not always as a result of the Egyptian *schistosoma, bilharzia,* but from other causes too.

Many of these diseases are very old. Let me read a few interesting passages from the Bible. As you look at them through medical eyes, entertain in your own mind what the writer is talking about. You, as physicians, are at a better advantage than the average layman who hears the same passages from a pulpit.

I will read from the book of Luke. As you know, St. Luke has been called the beloved physician; however, his book is not the language one would expect from an individual who attended a medical school. And, remember there were good medical schools in Egypt and in southern Greece over 300 years before St. Luke was born. When he draws a medical picture he uses few strokes, but bold ones, and the average third-year student in medicine would recognize it.

The following is an incident of Christ in the Synagogue. "Behold, there was a woman which had a spirit of infirmity eighteen years." [1] St. Luke picked the patient correctly, for this disease is far more frequent in women than in men. It wasn't a malignant disease nor was it tuberculosis. And remember there is evidence of a lot of tuberculosis existing at that period of time. It was, however, a disease of eighteen years, and apparently not of a vital organ. Then he gives it away.

"And was bowed together, and could in no wise lift up herself."

You have probably already recognized the disease as arthritis. The peripheral joints are involved, and she is bowed together, she couldn't lift up herself. That is the usual distribution in women, although it does, at times, occur in men. Men however, are far more prone to get the vertebral joints in trouble, rather than the peripheral joints.

We have found arthritis in Egypt, and in the eternally dry hot climate of middle Egypt, just as frequently as we have found it over the United States and North Europe.

Another instance in St. Luke, will give you an idea of how we interpret passages. Again, Christ was in the synagogue talking to a group.

"Behold, a man cried out saying: Master, I beseech Thee; look upon my son, for he is my only child." [2] What would be your reaction? The first thing you would say, would be: "Tell me something about him. What happened?" And I am sure that question was asked, because we have the answer to such a question:

"Lo, a spirit seizes him and he crieth, and then he foameth, and he bruiseth himself." Mark[3] cites this same instance by saying: "Sometimes he falls into the fire, and sometimes he falls into the water."

That is all we need to make a diagnosis of epilepsy. Do you know of any gadget that is of any help that Luke didn't have? The only thing that is lacking is the electro-encephalogram, and it was a little early for that. But, we still make the diagnosis by asking: "Did you ever hurt yourself? Did you ever bite your tongue, or fall down?"

Why do we ask that? Because, in medicine, we realize that in the hysterical convulsions of man or woman, they never fall without an audience or where it hurts. They are demonstrating.

At that period of time, the ancients believed God sent messages through these victims to the people on earth. And so, they seated someone beside him to jot down whatever he said no matter how incoherent, when he was coming out from the convulsion.

Mark gives an interesting commentary on medical practice, and I mention this because we frequently hear the same thing. How expensive medicine is: "And she had suffered many things of many physicians." [4] That is not unfamiliar, I know. Mark continues:

"And had spent all that she had on physicians." Then adding, "and was nothing bettered." And finally gives us a good slap with: "But she rather grew worse." I am sure we have all had that happen.

There are a great many references in the Bible, particularly in the Book of Proverbs, to the psychosomatic problems. There is nothing new in psychosomatic medicine, insofar as the actual practice of this branch of medicine is concerned. At present it is more clearly defined, but, we must concede its early origin. It has been practiced since man became a thinking creature. What are probably the basic or essential facts of psychosomatic medicine are effectively expressed in the Book of Proverbs.

"Hope deferred maketh the heart sick: but when the desire cometh, it is a tree of life." [5]

"Hope deferred." Isn't that frustration? That about which we worry? Over and over again we find that worry alters physiology. You know it, and so do I. Today, we don't use such simple terms as "Hope." However, it is perfectly adequate, in my opinion. We find instead of hope the term used in modern psychologic and psychiatric literature is "emotional support." Is this an improvement? Fewer people understand it!

There is one thing about the Biblical references that impresses me no end, and that is the fact the ancient Hebrew never kept his skeletons in the closet. When something unpleasant happened to his family, heroes or heroines, he never white-washed the facts. The Bible is a record of a people. They lived, much the same as you and I. Can't you picture the following quotation as the basis of altered physiology?

"Better is a dry morsel and quietness therewith, than a house full of sacrifices, with strife." [6]

"Better is a dinner of herbs where love is, than a stalled ox and hatred therewith." [7]

Doesn't that express it? The author also expresses it another way: "Better is a dinner of herbs, where love is, than a fatted ox and hatred therewith."

You know how true that is, and also that you can't express it better in any language.

What did you think about when you finished the physical examination of a patient? You were trying to rule out organic disease, which is the first demand on the part of the patient. After you felt you had ruled it out completely, you began to wonder, where is the trouble? Does it exist in the home, or is it where he works?—Where is the conflict? Where is the frustration? Where is the bickering? Where is the fighting? The man comes home with a good appetite, and a cross word is heard, or an argument ensues, his appetite is gone. These ancient people have all lived through that. Can't you picture them having an ulcer, as we know it today, essential hypertension, whatever that means or fluctuating pressure, all as the result of something occurring in their home?

And, if as the orthopaedists and surgeons tell us that most accidents happen in the home, then how much more true it is that the most emotional assaults and injuries also happen there. Perhaps we do not think about that phase of it, because they don't immediately cause a dramatic manifestation.

Let me read you another verse, and remember I didn't write this: "It is better to dwell in the wilderness than with a contentious and angry woman." That man lived, or he thought so!

This was not written by a woman because in my experience, I don't know whether or not it agrees with yours, I have seen and have been impressed constantly with the loyalty of women to their moral responsibilities. They spend twenty-four hours in their homes, whereas the man is out for eight or ten hours a day.

And, another thing, when we have a male patient with a colostomy, the family remains intact. However, if it is a woman, and the figures in Baltimore bear this out, there is more likely to be a divorce or separation. That never fails to impress me.

Again, there is the tremendous impulse of human affection, which surpasses any power that I am aware of today.

So that when I read this in Proverbs, I know that these people were like you and me. If they had feet of clay, they also rose to the heights. True, they were pock-marked, and most of them had all the diseases and the emotional instability that you and I are familiar with. We have good written records of such occurrences.

Before finishing, let me cite another interesting passage. This verse is found in the Book of Ezekiel. If you don't know your prophets, study them, because they are ethical as well as cultural giants, the best the world has ever produced.

On this occasion, Ezekiel was down in Babylonia. There, the King who was at the head of two ways was uncertain as to what he should do. And has this to say: "For the King of Babylon stood at the parting of the way, at the head of two ways to use divination: he made his arrows bright and he consulted with the images, he looked into the liver." [8] What do you think that means?

In the ancient days, when the doctor went to see his patient, the counselor or advisor for the family was asked about the prognosis. They did not care what Latin or Greek name was given the disease. These people were interested in what you could do about it. After the doctor finished his examination, he said: "Bring me in the liver."

The head of the household would kill a little lamb or goat, and bring the liver in on a platter. The liver of either a human or an animal contains 25 per cent of the blood, at any given time. Now, picture in your mind's eye, the body heat as vapor arising from it and a change of color taking place as a result of oxidation of the blood. The doctor would have a mental picture of a liver, or have a clay model of one beside him. Over the dome of these clay models of the liver were inscribed rectangles. Within each rectangle, in cuneiform, was the significance of the change of color inscribed. By comparing the actual liver with that of the model, the doctor made his prognosis. However, if your forefathers came from Northern Europe, they didn't look into the liver, but rather killed a bird, a pigeon or a chicken, then removed the intestinal tract. They based their prognosis on whether the peristaltic motion was rapid or slow, toward or away from the stomach.

Let me close with these fine passages. You should know them whether you are a doctor or not. Beside the medical interpretation of his work, we all have a stake in what the author is talking about:

"Remember, now, Thy Creator in the days of Thy youth, while the evil days come not, nor the years draw nigh, when thou shalt say: I have no pleasure in them.

"While the sun, or the light, or the moon, or the stars be not darkened, nor the clouds return after the rain: In the day when the keepers of the house shall tremble, and the strong men shall bow themselves, and the grinders cease because they are few, and those that look out of the windows be darkened.

"And the doors shall be shut in the street, when the sound of the grinding is low, and he shall rise up at the voice of the bird, and all the daughters of music shall be brought low.

"Also when they shall be afraid of that which is high, and fear shall be in the way, and the almond tree shall flourish, and the grasshopper shall be a burden, and the desire shall fail because man goeth to his long home and the mourners go about the street.

"Or ever the silver cord be loosed or the golden bowl be broken, or the pitcher be broken at the fountain, or the wheel broken at the cistern." [9]

Those of you who belong to certain organizations probably recite that. Do you know what you are talking about?

Let us look at it through medical eyes. We do know that the author is talking to young people. "Remember, now thy Creator in the days of Thy youth. . . ." You should think of your God, then, not when all these subsequent things happen to you. And he goes on:

"Remember, now, thy Creator in the days of Thy youth, while the evil days come not, nor the years draw nigh, when thou shalt say: I have no pleasure in them."

Isn't that true in old age? There is hardly a month that goes by in any city hospital, when some old patient doesn't say: "I am ready to go when my maker calls me. I have lived a long while, brought up a family, and enjoyed life."

But you don't find that in young people, and too, we would think that it was a serious mental aberration if we heard them talk in such a manner.

"Remember now thy Creator . . . while the sun, or the light, or the moon, or the stars be not darkened, nor the clouds return after the rain."

That is lovely imagery. Let us look at it through medical eyes, and human experience. If something happens in a young person's life, it is comparable to a thunder storm, darkness and flashes of lightning in the distance, then torrential rains; however, within an hour or so, the storm is over. The clouds part and the sky is blue again.

Let something happen in the old man's life. Let him lose his wife, his job, or his savings. Can he go out and recapture them? You know he cannot.

How is it expressed here? ". . . nor the clouds return after the rain." There is no blue in the sky for the old man. The

sky remains gray. And then the author becomes personal. The
oriental and Biblical writers in particular refer to the body as
the temple in which the soul dwells.

"In the day when the keepers of the house shall tremble, and
the strong men shall bow themselves, and the grinders shall
cease because they are few, and those that look out of the
windows be darkened."

The keepers of my body and your body, obviously, are the
hands, and when do these keepers of your house tremble? When
do you get arteriosclerotic tremor, shaking, palsy, with increased
frequency? As you grow older.

". . . when the keepers of the house shall tremble and the
strong men shall bow themselves."

"And the strong men shall bow themselves."

We need a foundation, the same as this building does. The
foundations of your body and mine are the legs; you know the
bowing attitude of the legs in the older man, and when does it
happen? ". . . when the keepers of the house shall tremble, and
the strong men shall bow themselves, and the grinders cease
because they are few. . . ."

When do your teeth fall out? You know the answer. Don't you
see how personal the author gets in his description? His answer is
medically correct, as we grow older.

Then he goes on and says that those who look out of the
window will be darkened. If my body is that temple there are
only two windows to that body, and they are the eyes. There
is a perfectly good Hebrew word for eyes, but the oriental writer
always loves good imagery; those eyes are the windows. And,
when do you hold things farther and farther away? When do
you get cataracts? As you grow older. The imagery is lovely.

"And the doors shall be shut in the street. . . ."

Now, if you wanted to keep the noise out of this building,
you would close the door into the street. And, if I am talking
about my body, there are only two doors in my body that admit
noise within it, the ears. You know how the older people cup
their ears in order to hear.

Then he adds the time when deafness usually comes on,
namely, when the sound of the grinding is low, when the teeth
have fallen out.

". . . and he shall rise up at the voice of the bird, and all the daughters of music shall be brought low."

Who gets up early in your house, the youngsters or the older people?

The reference to the daughters of music is the imagery used in the middle east for the night clubs—the daughters of music, the dancing girls, the cabaret girls. As we grow older, there is usually the waning of interest in this side of life; I am sure no night club in your city is attended by many of 70, 75 and 80 years old.

"Also when they shall be afraid of that which is high, and fear shall be in the way. . . ."

That is sound isn't it? It is the caution of the aged. For, remember, that without that caution, you may never get to be an older man or woman.

". . . . the almond tree shall flourish. . . ." That is the gray hair. And we also see the waning of sex, as we grow older. ". . . and the grasshopper shall be a burden and desire shall fail . . ." The grasshopper is a sex symbol and the final clause "desire shall fail" clearly refers to the sex desire. Remember, this was written before the days of hormones.

". . . because man goeth to his long home, and the mourners go about the street." After all of this happens we usually pass on. However, if you haven't passed on by this time, he adds another verse:

"Or ever the silver cord be loosed. . . ." We have to suspend judgment a bit on that, depending upon which framework of time you interpret it. But, in either event, it has something to do with coordination.

". . . or the golden bowl be broken, . . ." That is not the brain. There isn't a reference in the Old or the New Testament to the brain having a function. It is a curious thing; they saw skulls on the battlefield; they saw their animals' skulls bashed open too, but they never placed a function in the brain. The emotions, the spirit, the sentimental part of the individual was located most commonly in the kidney, and in less frequency in the liver. The term "melancholia or back bile" is responsible for the depressed spirit. Least frequently, it was the heart.

In any event, whether it is the kidney, the liver or the heart

when the ". . . golden bowl is broken, . . ." it is near the end of
the rainbow of life.

". . . or the pitcher be broken at the fountain. . . ."

The imagery and the context there suggests the organs of
watery excretion. What produces water in our bodies? The kid-
neys. Not where water is collected, but the fountain producing it.

The next part should be interpreted along with this:

". . . or the wheel broken at the cistern." Where the water is
collected and not produced—isn't that our problem in the aged,
in the matter of retention in one and incontinence in the other.
There is much lovely imagery in that classical prose.

After all of this has happened: "Then shall the dust return
to the earth as it was; and the spirit shall return unto God,
who gave it."

I wish the writer would have talked about the psychology of
old men; but the man who caught that best was Oliver Wendell
Holmes, a doctor in Boston, not many miles from here. He
described a beautiful picture in his poem about an old neighbor
who passed by the door every morning, when he took his walk: [10]

> And I saw him once before
> As he passed by the door
>   and again
> The pavement stones resound
> As he totters o'er the ground
>   With his cane.
>
> They say that in his prime,
> E're the pruning knife of time
>   Cut him down,
> Not a better man was found
> By the crier on his round
>   Through the town.
>
> But now he walks the streets
> And he looks at all he meets
>   Sad and wan,
> And he shakes his feeble head,
> That it seems as if he said,
>   "They are gone."

The mossy marbles rest
On the lips that he has prest
    In their bloom,
And the names he loved to hear
Have been carved for many a year
    On the tomb.

My grandmama has said—
Poor old lady, she is dead
    Long ago—
That he had a Roman nose,
And his cheek was like a rose
    In the snow.
But now his nose is thin
And it rests upon his chin
    Like a staff.
And a crook is in his back
And a melancholy crack
    In his laugh.

I know it is a sin
For me to sit and grin
    At him here;
But the old three cornered hat,
And the breeches, and all that,
    Are so queer!

And if I should live to be
The last leaf upon the tree
    In the Spring,
Let them smile as I do now
At the old forsaken bough
    Where I cling.

REFERENCES

1 Luke 13, 11   6 Proverbs 17, 1
2 Luke 9, 38   7 Proverbs 15, 17
3 Mark 9, 18   8 Ezekiel 21, 21
4 Mark 5, 26   9 Ecclesiastes 12, 1
5 Proverbs 13, 12   10 Holmes, O. W.: The Last Leaf.

6

The Superior Clinical Acumen of the Old Physicians

A Myth

JOHN W. TODD, M.D., M.R.C.P.

R EFERENCES are often made to a race of great physicians who flourished some fifty years ago. Though lacking such modern aids to diagnosis as radiography, laboratory investigations, and 'scopes and other instruments, they were, we are led to understand, nevertheless able to reach the correct diagnosis in a high proportion of cases solely by their clinical skill at the bedside. Their dexterity of touch and their acuity of hearing, sight, and smell, acquired by years of patient training of the senses, were such that they were able to detect—and interpret correctly— subtle physical signs which are beyond the grasp of the comparatively ill developed clinical faculties of the doctors of today.

It is now taken for granted that the final diagnostic court of appeal for organic diseases is the pathological or bacteriological evidence. Such evidence is often not available, but in a high proportion of serious, and particularly fatal, illnesses it can sooner or later be found. But in the days of the great physicians such evidence could rarely be obtained from the living, and when obtained from the dead it was not nearly so complete as it is today. It follows that the final court of appeal—at least when the patient was not fatally ill—was the bedside diagnosis. When an eminent physician, called down from London, diagnosed the threat of consumption, incipient brain fever, diaphragmatic gout, or strained heart the matter no doubt seemed settled. The old physicians, therefore, may have been generally judged to be right when in fact they were wrong. And they could afford to be confident in their diagnoses; the present-day physician is con-

Reprinted from THE LANCET, March 7, 1953, p. 482

strained, by the possibility of subsequent pathological findings, to be more cautious.

THE VALUE OF PHYSICAL SIGNS

The reputation of the old physicians chiefly depended on their ability to discover and interpret physical signs. It is sometimes suggested that learning to appreciate many signs, particularly those arising from the chest, is very difficult. The beginner, it is said, when examining with the greatest care a case of early pulmonary tuberculosis, may detect nothing wrong. Whereas the expert, with the aid of his trained senses of hearing and vision, may be able to find an occasional râle, a slightly prolonged expiratory sound, minor variations in the percussion note, almost imperceptible flattening of one part of the chest, and slight impairment of movement of one side. But such inconspicuous signs are hardly significant. Variations between the chest appearances of normal people, or in the same individual between different parts of the chest, are surely as great as are those presented by many of these signs. They do not justify the diagnosis of pulmonary tuberculosis if the radiograph is normal in every view and the sputum is free of tubercle bacilli; and if there is real evidence of the disease they should not influence the opinion of the state of the chest. Similar criticism can be made of other inconspicuous signs, such as slight pallor of an optic disc, an equivocal plantar response on both sides, a "slapping" first heart sound, or an increased area of splenic dullness on percussion. If there are other reasons for coming to a diagnosis their aid is not required; if they are alone they justify no diagnosis. Trivial deviations from the average can be discovered in any man if they are looked for hard enough.

The appreciation of physical signs is, then, not the difficult matter it is sometimes held to be. The signs of real value are those which are striking, and which anyone, *provided he seeks for them,* can appreciate.

Obvious signs are nevertheless often not discovered, for the simple reason that they have not been sought. This may especially happen when they were absent at first but developed later. A patient may reveal manifestations suggesting carcinoma of the lung. The chest is examined over and over again, repeated radiographs are taken, much sputum is sent to the laboratory, and bronchography and bronchoscopy are performed. Yet when in the end all these examinations and investigations have confirmed the presence of a carcinoma, no-one may have noticed that a hard mass of glands has become palpable above the clavicle —glands which were not present in the earlier stages.

Does then the idea that the old physicians were better than the new rest on their superior thoroughness in seeking for signs? No doubt many modern doctors do not examine their patients with sufficient thoroughness, but hasten instead to employ radiography and other aids to diagnosis. But shirking the physical examination cannot always be condemned. When a patient has an injured leg it may be possible to demonstrate a fracture by eliciting crepitus between the bone ends. This is a far less certain method than is an X-ray photograph and it may be highly unpleasant, and possibly dangerous, for the patient. A fair comparison between the old and the modern physicians in their ability to discover signs can only be made when signs are as relevant now as they were in the past. Although this comparison is very difficult to draw it may be conceded that the old physicians were superior, because they did not start with the assumption, as many modern doctors do, that special investigations inevitably count for more than clinical examination.

The main problem presented by physical signs is their interpretation. And this requires two distinct stages: first, deciding what is the cause of the sign; and second, deciding whether this cause is responsible for the symptoms. A double error of interpretation may even be made with a single sign. An apical systolic murmur may be discovered in a patient complaining of palpitation, left mammary pain, rapid beating of the heart, and sighing respiration. The wrong deduction may first be made that the sign is due to mitral regurgitation, and next it may be wrongly concluded that such symptoms are caused by this lesion. The first stage of interpretation is undoubtedly important, but more attention should be paid to the second stage. Too often is it casually assumed that some lesion is responsible for a patient's symptoms when this is not so; and too often are diagnoses made, right in the sense that the conditions thought to be present are present, but wrong because they do not explain why the patients feel ill.

Were the old physicians superior to the new in their ability to interpret physical signs? On the contrary, it seems that some of them put unjustified interpretation upon signs, particularly on those arising from the chest, for they are often non-specific phenomena which may be due to many different pathological states. Many old signs, such as the *tache cerebrale* and Campbell de Morgan's spots, are now known to be valueless. And there does not seem to have been in the past a widespread realisation of the existence of the second stage in the interpretation of physical signs.

THE RELEVANCE OF SYMPTOMS

Symptoms, other than those obviously due to local causes such as boils, piles, or dental caries or to grave illnesses, are not so easy to interpret as physical signs and the results of special investigations. To analyse them successfully, the observer has to possess the ability to appreciate the feelings of others, who may be stupid, unable to express themselves and describe their sensations, or even wilfully misleading. Yet the symptoms can be supremely important in diagnosis. Anginal pain, for example, may be the only definite manifestation of coronary-artery disease, and is often far more valuable than the other findings.

When symptoms are unaccompanied by other evidence of disease, there is a modern tendency to consider them imaginary or neurotic. This last conclusion may often be true, though the reason for reaching it should not be the absence of evidence of bodily disease but the discovery of positive evidence of psychological disorder and the demonstration of how the symptoms are due to this disorder. Formerly such symptoms were often wrongly attributed to disorder of the organ where they arose; and this practice is still far from dead. The old physicians often ascribed palpitation, aching in the precordial region, sighing respiration, fatigue and giddiness (which in reality appear to be bound up with temperamental upsets and unrelated to disease of the heart) to heart strain, disordered action of the heart, tired heart, and, with even less justification, to valvular heart disease, especially when a systolic murmur happened to be present. Sir Thomas Lewis after the first world war gave the classical description of the enormous scale of this error in relation to soldiers.

In the field of interpreting symptoms unaccompanied by other findings, therefore, the old physicians were not superior, and were probably much inferior, to the new. If now symptoms are sometimes wrongly minimised, in the past, they were often wrongly ascribed to fanciful pathological causes.

WHAT IS A CORRECT DIAGNOSIS?

I concluded elsewhere [1] that it is wrong to assume that it is usually possible to make a pathological diagnosis. Apart from the patients with somatic symptoms of psychological origin, a high proportion of complaints, especially pains in the limbs and back, headache, and much dyspepsia, cannot yet be related to pathological states. Moreover, when the symptoms have some pathological basis, a bald pathological label does not represent their whole cause; the state of mind must also be taken into consideration, particularly when the lesion is chronic and comparatively benign. A hallux valgus does not wholly explain pain in the foot on walking; and the end-results of the treatment of this condition are determined by the patient's temperament as well as by the severity of the lesion and the nature of the operation.

In olden days the proportion of disorders without a known pathological basis was higher than it is today. Yet the reputation of the old physicians does not rest upon their ability to recognise and classify conditions of this kind; nor did they seem to lay great stress on the importance of psychological factors even when some pathological state was present. On the contrary, the stories of their prowess are mostly about their ability to diagnose gross, and especially fatal, pathological lesions.

Leaving considerations of this kind aside (which means ignoring a high proportion of diagnostic problems) and viewing diagnosis solely as a process of identifying some gross pathological lesion, it must be asked what is, in any particular circumstance, a correct diagnosis? It cannot be disputed that the most searching clinical examination by the most brilliant diagnostician may not reveal sufficient data to reach a confident conclusion. Later developments may provide an answer, but until then the diagnosis should be tentative. A patient may have fever lacking any special characteristics such as those of malaria, no physical signs, and no symptoms save the general ones of fever. Clearly there are numerous possibilities, including enteric fever, brucellosis, Hodgkin's disease, pyelitis, infective endocarditis, and various kinds of septicæmia. A physician may make an inspired guess that one of these conditions is present, and, if subsequent developments confirm his guess, his feat may appear most impressive. Although he turned out to be right, his diagnosis was in reality wrong because it was formed on insufficient grounds. The correct provisional diagnosis here was the bald "pyrexia of undetermined origin." A similar conclusion can be reached of many other diagnostic problems, such as the "acute abdomen" and the chest possibly the seat of malignant disease.

Often, therefore, a definite diagnosis is unjustified, and the best diagnostic statement is provided by a review of the various conditions which could explain all the available data; though often it will also be sound to conclude that some condition is highly probable, others are possible, others improbable, and others conceivable. The reputation of many of the old physicians does not depend on their reaching cautious conclusions of this kind, but on their dogmatic statements that the diagnosis is such and such a disease.

It should also be remembered that diagnosis is not an end in itself, but a means to providing treatment or making prognoses. In the last century specific medical treatment hardly existed, and until towards the end of it there was little effective surgery. It was perhaps because of this that diagnosis came to be considered so supremely important, since the physician was almost impotent to do anything but diagnose. And there then existed a host of futile or dangerous remedies persisting from a more ignorant epoch, and the physician who was a therapeutic nihilist as regards these remedies was clearly superior to his less critical colleague who still continued to use them. Now we have such a large number of highly effective, and often life-saving, drugs and so many excellent surgical procedures that the old doctrine which emphasised the importance of making an accurate diagnosis before giving treatment is far from universally applicable. For example, some patients with undiagnosed high fever should be treated blindly, especially when malignant tertian malaria is a possibility, for the failure to discover parasites in the peripheral blood proves nothing, the untreated disease is often fatal, and the specific drugs for malaria are highly effective and can do no harm to those without malaria. The desperately ill patient with swinging fever may rightly be given penicillin while undiagnosed. And a reasonable suspicion of amœbic hepatitis justifies the giving of emetine. Indeed, the possible presence of a potentially fatal disease, or a disease liable to cause permanent sequelæ, which cannot certainly be excluded and is susceptible to some specific remedy, provides sufficient reason for giving that remedy while the diagnosis is still in doubt. Moreover, the study of the remedy's effect can itself often be diagnostic. The failure of fever to respond to quinine provides virtual proof that malaria is not the cause of fever.

A physician cannot, then, be judged, as the old physicians often seem to have been judged, solely by his ability to reach precise diagnoses, for the following reasons:

(1) In a high proportion of cases no pathological diagnosis can be made.

(2) When a pathological lesion, especially if chronic and benign, is related to the symptoms, the mere identification of this lesion does not make a complete diagnosis, since the state of mind, which is partly responsible for the symptoms, must also be considered.

(3) When a patient clearly has organic disease there are often insufficient data to reach a precise diagnosis, and the best diagnostic statement is represented, not by a guess at a likely diagnosis, but by a review of the various possibilities.

(4) Diagnosis is not an end in itself, but the means to an end. It is often right to give treatment when diagnosis is but tentative and the effect of treatment may itself be diagnostic.

DISCUSSION

If my arguments have been sound, the concept of the old physician at the bedside reaching diagnoses with his unaided senses and his clinical acumen, which the modern physician can reach only with the help of elaborate investigations—if even then—belongs, not to history, but to mythology.

Perhaps the main reason why this myth arose is to be found in the natural habit of young men of looking up to their elders. The impressionable student or resident feels that his Chief clearly knows so much more than he does himself that he may come to accept his word as law. In later years he may often be conscious of the profound difficulty of medicine, and realise how frequently he cannot decide what is the matter with patients, or what should be done for them. His reason may suggest that his Chiefs were also in similar dilemmas, but it may nevertheless be difficult to get rid of the deep feeling that they *knew*, and that when they pronounced a diagnosis they were right. When in his turn he instructs students, he may hand on stories of their infallibility, which become part of the folk-lore of the medical school. Towards their own contemporaries, on the other hand, men are much more critical. They may readily admit that some-one they do not know is a genius in a subject of which they know little, but few are conscious that one of their own friends may be a genius in their own subject. Jealousy, too, tends to be responsible for the belittlement of contemporaries; but people feel little jealousy towards a distinguished old man, and none at all towards the dead.

There is nevertheless some truth in the view that all is not well with modern medicine. A common error is the widespread assumption that the results of elaborate investigations are inevitably superior to the clinical evidence, and particularly to the evidence of symptoms. A figure derived from the pathological laboratory, or a shadow on a radiographic plate, is too often thought to represent exact truth. Investigations are increasingly done routinely, and in medical schools this practice may be excused on the ground that the investigations are desirable for the sake of the students, though hardly necessary for the welfare of the patient. Why to give students the impression that the nation's money and the patient's time should be wasted in performing tests which do not help, and may be unpleasant and alarming, is not clear. Many doctors apparently never ask themselves the question "whatever the possible results of this investigation, will my opinion be affected?"

The emphasis wrongly put upon investigations at present is of a piece with the emphasis wrongly put upon many physical signs in the past. What is needed now, as it was then, is a proper sense of balance. Each patient should be considered as an individual clinical problem. Routine history-taking and routine physical examination, according to a standard formula, are just as mistaken as is routine investigation. In some cases, such as possible hæmophilia, a searching family history may be most valuable. In many others, particularly when there are numerous complaints reaching far into the past, a careful study of the symptoms and of personal relationships may be all-important. But when there is one predominant symptom of short duration pointing to an accessible region of the body—as with whitlows, sore throat, and piles—the physical examination is supreme, and the remainder almost or quite valueless. And when the symptoms suggest organic disease in a region likely to produce no physical sign, or physical signs of indefinite character—as when pulmonary tuber-culosis, enteric fever, and urinary infection are suspect—certain special investigations are clearly indicated.

* * *

Although in this paper I have attacked the view that the old physicians, by their skill in appreciating and interpreting physical signs, were able to make diagnoses of which we are incapable, it is not my intention to belittle the great advances which many of them made. They *discovered* the physical signs and began their study and the assessment of their significance. An impor-tant reason why we can do better than they did is that we are in the fortunate position of enjoying the fruits of their labours.

SUMMARY AND CONCLUSIONS

The belief that the old physicians of fifty years ago were able solely by their skill at the bedside to reach diagnoses which modern clinicians can reach only with the aid of elaborate inves-tigations is examined and dismissed. Only in one field—namely the discovery of physical signs—has there possibly been a decline in recent years, and in most other respects there has been an advance. Nevertheless a common error of modern medicine is the assumption that the results of special investigations are nec-essarily superior to the clinical findings, and particularly to the symptoms.

The views expressed on the appreciation, discovery, and interpretation of physical signs were previously published elsewhere.[2] I wish to thank my father for his help in revision, and Dr. C. C. Thomas for his advice and criticism.

REFERENCES
1. Todd, J. W.: *Lancet,* 1952, ii, 1235.
2. Todd, J. W.: Rational Medicine. Bristol, 1949.

7

Record of the Case

SIR JOHN CHARLES, M.D., F.R.C.P., D.P.H.

At 8 o'clock on the evening of Thursday, October 24, 1867, Wagner scored the final bars of *Die Meistersinger*, inscribed the time and date, and laid down his pen.

Without any comparable marking of the chronology, but just as conclusively, a Theban scribe set aside his pen 3600 years ago, "in the middle of a line, in the middle of a sentence, in the middle of a word." His task had been the copying of an old surgical treatise, written in its primordial form at least a thousand years earlier.

Five hundred years before this scribe began his labours, a commentator had added to the original text an interpretation of some of its archaic words and phrases, and these glosses too were transcribed on to the roll of reed paper, which we know as the Edwin Smith Surgical Papyrus.

The treatise was in essence a catalogue of 48 surgical cases, all males, and many of them warriors. The descriptions of the surgical experiences of those patients are in the conventional sense of the words, our earliest medical records. The grouping of the 48 cases suggests that they were part of a larger collection. Commencing with the head and skull, they next include the neck, clavicles, humerus, sternum, and spinal column—and then cease abruptly. The logic of the descriptive scheme envisages a commentary on the surgery of the thorax, abdomen, and lower members. But some event or person interrupted the work of the scribe. He evidently contemplated the resumption of his copying, for a stretch of 31 inches of virgin papyrus was left between his unfinished task and the engrossing of a collection of incantations and medicinal and cosmetic recipes.

Not only was there order and method in the planning of the

Opening address at the First International Congress on Medical Records. London, Sept. 8, 1952.

Reprinted from THE LANCET, June 6, 1953, p. 1141

treatise, but the presentation of each case conformed to a simple pattern. First there came an identification of the case; next a statement of the examination; then a diagnosis and a tentative prognosis in three ascending degrees of severity—an ailment that could be treated, an ailment that could be contended with, an ailment not suitable for treatment. Finally, the treatment was prescribed. Here is the record of a simple case—a broken nose.

If thou examinest a man having a break in the column of his nose, his nose being disfigured, and a depression being in it, while the swelling that is on it protrudes, and he has discharged blood from both his nostrils—thou shouldst say concerning him "an ailment which I will treat."

Thou shouldst cleanse it for him with two plugs of linen. Thou shouldst place two other plugs of linen saturated with grease inside of his two nostrils. Thou shouldst put him at his mooring stakes until the swelling is reduced. Thou shouldst apply for him stiff rolls of linen by which his nose is held fast. Thou shouldst treat him afterwards with grease, honey and lint every day until he recovers.

The hand of the gloss-writer has explained the unusual simile— "put him at his mooring stakes" means putting him on his customary diet, without administering a prescription.

Of the 48 cases described, no more than 15 were assigned to the category of the hopeless, and in 1 instance only did the practitioner substitute magic and incantations for surgery.

The Hippocratic Corpus

Twelve hundred years after the unfinished business of the Edwin Smith Surgical Papyrus, there was accumulated in Greece a very different collection of medical and epidemiological knowledge. This corpus of writings, a vertible library of treatises, aphorisms, case-histories, and the like, is associated with the name of Hippocrates. How much is attributable to Hippocrates himself one cannot now say, but the collection represents the thoughts and experiences of tough minds and keen observers.

Here again we have a group of medical records to study, and on this occasion surgery is joined by medicine and midwifery and the patients are freemen and slaves, men, women and children often identified by name or domicile. The celebrated clinical picture-gallery of the first and third books of *Epidemics* displays 42 cases, 25 of them fatal. They are preceded by brisk,

critical commentaries, the so-called constitutions, which discuss
in general terms the meterological conditions of the respective
seasons, the epidemic disorders which were prevalent, their trends
and features. So we find it recorded that in the spring of some
undatable year

> Many had swellings beside one ear, or both ears, in most cases unattended
> with fever, so that confinement to bed was unnecessary. In some cases there
> was slight heat, but in all the swellings subsided without causing harm. . . .
> This was the character of them—flabby, big, spreading with neither inflam-
> mation nor pain. . . . The sufferers were youths, young men, and men in
> their prime, usually those who frequented the wrestling school and gymnasia.
> Few women were attacked.

Then follow in no particular order and in varying detail the
clinical histories and descriptions of the patients.

Lastly, as an appendix to the majority of cases in the third
book of *Epidemics,* we encounter a sort of registrar's summary, a
synoptic line of a few Greek capital letters, which gives the duration, outcome, and character—that is the operative word—of the
disease. Seven such capitals epitomised the death from fever and
diarrhœa of a woman who seven days previously had had a
miscarriage.

The 42 case-histories of those two books of *Epidemics* have
been described as the most remarkable product of Greek science.
They differ markedly from the records of the Edwin Smith
papyrus. Their breadth of clinical interest is greater; the presentation of the case is fuller; the statement of personal and social
detail is more elaborate. But their outstanding distinction is to
be seen in the cool day-by-day study of the progress of the pathological phenomena in the body of the patient. Often the
phrases which record these changes have caught for all time
the physiognomy of disease or the prolegomena of dissolution.
Oddly enough, in comparison with Egyptian practice, there is a
virtual omission of any reference to treatment.

That combination of calm observation and apparent implicit
reliance on the curative powers of Nature has given rise to the
suggestion that the Hippocratic casebook is little more than a
"meditation upon death." Such comment is not altogether fair,
because in another of the books of the corpus, the *Regimen in
Acute Disease,* the cardinal remedies are adequately described.

Amongst the diseases met with are examples of those protean Mediterranean malarial fevers, of puerperal and wound infections, of the pneumonias and dysenteries, and of several strange delirious states which cannot be precisely identified. Here are two specimens of these records, as brief and succinct as any in the collection:

(a) Crito, in Thasos, while walking about, was seized with a violent pain in the great toe. He took to bed the same day with shivering and nausea; regained a little warmth; at night was delirious.

Second day. Swelling of the whole foot, which was rather red about the ankle, and distended; black blisters; acute fever; mad delirium. Alvine discharges unmixed, bilious and rather frequent. He died on the second day from the commencement.

(b) Another woman, after a miscarriage about the fifth month, the wife of Hicetas, was seized with fever. At the beginning she had alternations of coma and sleeplessness; pain in the loins; heaviness in the head.

Second day. Bowels disordered with scanty, thin stools, which at first were uncompounded.

Third day. Stools more copious and worse; no sleep at night.

Fourth day. Delirium; fears; depression. Squinting of the right eye; slight cold sweat about the head; extremities cold.

Fifth day. General exacerbation; much wandering, with rapid recovery of reason; no thirst; no sleep; stools copious and unfavourable throughout; urine scanty, thin and blackish; extremities cold and rather livid.

Sixth day. Same symptoms.

Seventh day. Death.

The shorthand epitome of this second case requires eight Greek capital letters.

These are crisp, comprehensive narratives, composed by an alert eye-witness. Medical literature, except in rare examples, shows nothing like them for the next 1700 years.

THE MIDDLE AGES

After them came that long dark vista of the earlier Middle Ages. Here and there in the ancient and medieval chronicles, amongst the "sad stories of the death of Kings," there are credible accounts of the last illnesses of the royal and the great, sufficient to provide the material for a diagnosis. Such descriptions, however, are too infrequent to be regarded as a fruitful source of information for our present purpose.

THE RENAISSANCE

Medical recording had to wait until 1507 for its renaissance. That year saw the publication of the posthumous masterpiece of the Florentine physician, Antonio Benivieni, *De abditis nonnullis ac mirandis morborum et santationum causis*. The discussions of the hidden causes derive from a study of 24 postmortem examinations, and each individual finding is linked to a short description of the earlier clinical assessment of the patient.

In this simple form of correlation we can see the germ of the clinicopathological conference of today, and Benivieni as the precursor of the Cabots.

If royal mortality provided an indifferent field for research, there is, at any rate, one satisfactory piece of detailed medical history writing which leaves little unsaid about the health and habits of James I of England. The author was Theodore Turquet de Mayerne, a Swiss, who commenced practice in Paris, became physician-in-ordinary to the then King of France, Henry IV, and in 1611 was invited to England to take up the appointment of first physician to its monarch.

The memorandum "On the preservation of the King's health," a document of upwards of 4000 words, was written in December, 1623, two years before the King's death. It is as candid and thorough an appreciation of the psychology and pathology of a human being, albeit a King, as ever pen communicated to paper. For any historian of the troubles of the Stuart dynasty, this portrait is of ætiological significance, but, in this context, only a few of its passages need be quoted from Sir Norman Moore's translation. It commences thus:

James the First, King of Great Britain, was born at Edinburgh in the year 1566, on June 19th, at half-past eleven in the morning, and is now aged over 57 years. He had a drunken wet-nurse and was suckled for about a year. He has a very steadfast brain, which was never disturbed by the sea, by drinking wine, or by driving in a coach.

He is easily affected by cold and suffers in cold and damp weather. His chest is broad and well formed, and the vital parts contained therein have strong and lively warmth and never are afflicted unless as a result of morbid conditions elsewhere. The liver naturally good, large, of much blood, warm, liable to obstructions, and inclined to generate much bile. The spleen now easily heaps up melancholic juice, the presence of which is indicated by various symptoms. There is no swelling in either of these viscera and no hardness.

Each hypochondrium is soft and never distended, except with wind. The stomach is always ready for the burden of a large quantity of food and is prompt to get rid of any hurtful excess, chiefly by the bowel.

His legs seem not strong enough to sustain the weight of the body. His habit loose and of pervious texture, and he readily heats with dry heat. Skin thin and delicate, so that it itches easily. Fauces narrow, causing difficulty in swallowing, which defect is hereditary from his mother and grandfather James V of Scotland.

Air.—His Majesty bears all changes of air fairly well; in damp weather with a south wind he is attacked by catarrh.

Food.—As regards food he does not much amiss except that he eats no bread. He generally takes roast meats. Owing to want of teeth he does not chew his food but bolts it. Fruit he eats at all hours of day and night.

Drink.—In drinks he errs as to quality, quantity, frequency, time, and order. He promiscuously drinks beer, ale, Spanish wine, sweet French wine, white wine (his normal drink), and Muscatelle wine (whence he has diarrhœa), and sometimes Alicant wine. Nevertheless, he does not mind whether wine be strong or no so it be sweet. He has the strongest antipathy to water and all watery drinks.

Affections of the mind.—His mind is easily moved suddenly. He is very wrothful, but the fit soon passes off. Sometimes he is melancholy from the spleen in the left hypochondrium exciting disorders.

Excreta.—He often blows his nose, sneezes very often. Does not spit much unless from catarrh. Stomach easily made sick if he retains undigested food or bile. Vomits with great effort, so that after being sick his face appears for a day or two spotted with red spots. Much wind. Vapours from his stomach precede illness. The alvine discharge is uncertain and depends on the nature of his food, which often produces morbid changes. A tendency to looseness gets rid of a burden produced by what he has eaten.

Former illnesses and present aptitude to various morbid dispositions.—The King to the sixth year of his age was not able to walk, but was carried about, so weak was he from the bad milk of his drunken nurse. Between the second and fifth year he had smallpox and measles. In his fifth year for twenty-four hours he had suppression of urine, nevertheless no sand or slime was ejected.

He is of extreme sensitiveness, most impatient of pains; and while they torture him with most violent movements his mind is tossed, and bile flows around his præcordia, whence the evil is not relieved, but made worse.

He demands relief and freedom from pain, little considering about the causes of his illness.

As to remedies.—The King laughs at medicine, and holds it so cheap that he declares physicians to be of very little use and hardly necessary. He asserts the art of medicine to be supported by mere conjecturs, and useless because uncertain.

Mayerne, with his uncanny observation and assiduous *curatio* —he proposed a placebo for every trivial symptom—nevertheless paid tribute to ancient and medieval doctrines. For him catarrh

descends from the brain to produce coryza, the humours boil in
the stomach, and the spleen from its seat in the left hypochondrium excites disorders. More than seven years before Mayerne
completed his memorandum, William Harvey had already pro-
claimed the circulation of the blood. And with its ultimate
general acceptance physiology shook off the strings of Galen,
and medicine began, however tentatively, to take its modern
shape.

The experimental method established itself; logical reasoning
replaced speculative opinion; cause and effect began to be brack-
eted together in the minds of the medical faculty.

MORGAGNI

Let us skip another century and take counsel of Giovanni
Battista Morgagni, chief professor of anatomy at Padua and
president of the university. He obtained his first appointment
in Padua in 1712, and there remained for over fifty years, amass-
ing reputation and honours as anatomist, pathologist, physician,
man of affairs, and philosopher. He died in his ninetieth year
in 1771, ten years after the publication of his monument, "more
durable than brass," the great repository of medical and pathological experience entitled *De sedibus et causis morborum*. In
that great work, clinical histories march side by side with the
revelations of the post-mortem table, and wherever possible a
correlation is established between them. "The Seats and Causes"
is in construction a collection of 70 letters, each dealing with a
separate subject or disorder. It runs to about a million and a
half of words, mentions many hundreds of individual patients
both "intra-vitam" and "post-mortem," and rejoices the heart
of the reader by the provision of four comprehensive and associated indexes.

In the introduction Morgagni modestly introduces both himself and the original recipient of the letters:

I have not dwelt long upon explications, and have taken care to intersperse
other remarks relative to the practice of medicine, some of which relate to
the history thereof, and some to the history of anatomy, and finally, many
things which relate to the pursuits and studies of the young gentleman to
whom I addressed the letters, and this with an intention to withdraw his
imagination for a while, from the horrid and perpetual idea of diseases and
dead bodies.

There is a Chaucerian flavour about the citizens of Morgagni's world. Little phrases etch and identify them. Here are some of the patients:

A nobleman of Bologna; a woman of 40 years of age of a fleshy habit but a sallow colour, having eaten onions; an ostler, near sixty years of age, tall and fat, being used to eat much and drink very freely; a woman of Padua, by name Jacoba, the wife of Angelo Zanardi—finding 13 ribs on each side of her; a monk who was noble both in his birth and his manners; a woman of 75 years of age, of a manly aspect and very fat; a certain man skilled in the art of music, and the use of its instruments.

The first of the 70 letters is inscribed "Of Pain in the head." It parades before us "A boy of 13 years of age, of a ready wit, whose brother and sister had died of a consumption" followed by "a man about 40 years of age, (who) had been liable for many years to a pain in the right hypochondrium." "To those two histories," continues Morgagni, "give me leave to add a third, which though it does not relate to a man but a sheep is far from being unworthy of our notice."

Where there is such a wealth of material it is difficult to select. From over 700 necropsies, here are three histories, neither better recorded nor more brilliantly depicted than scores of others. Each is in its way notable. The first is probably the original picture of the Stokes-Adams syndrome; similarly, the second is an early, if not the earliest record of a patient in the grip of "angina pectoris"; the third vividly recounts the rupture of an aortic aneurysm.

I

"A merchant at Padua of 64 years of age, of a square stature, and of a fat habit of body, but not to excess. He having been formerly subject to a rheumatism . . . had been cured by medicinal remedies: so that notwithstanding he was taken up with many and various businesses continually, he was, nevertheless, in good health; when of a sudden he was seized with very violent affections of the mind. . . .

"A few days after these commotions, a kind of vertigo coming on, he fell down—and on the day following he began to be troubled with convulsive motions, together with an attack similar to epilepsy. . . ."

After several months during which the patient improved and then relapsed, Morgagni's services as a physician were asked for. He writes: "whom visiting by way of consultation I found with such a rarity of the pulse that within the sixtieth part of an hour the pulsations were only 22—and this rareness which was perpetual . . . was perceived to be even more considerable, as often as even two (epileptic) attacks were at hand—so that the physicians were never deceived, if from the increase of the rareness they foretold a paroxysm to be coming on."

II

"The mother of a family, who was two and forty years of age—had long been subject to a kind of paroxysm, which appeared in the following manner: on using pretty quick exercise of body, a kind of violent uneasiness came on, within the upper part of the thorax on the left side, joined with a difficulty of breathing, and a stupor of the left arm, all which symptoms soon remitted when those motions ceased. This woman then, having set out . . . from Venice to go up the continent in a wheeled carriage, and being cheerful in her mind, behold the same paroxysm returned, . . . and saying that she should die, she actually died on the spot."

At the post mortem Morgagni found "the Aorta—not a little dilated at the curvature" with "compleat bony scales," of a small size; not to mention frequent marks of ossification being begun.

III

"A man who had been too much given to the exercise of tennis and the abuse of wine, was . . . seized with a pain of the right arm, and soon after of the left joined with a fever. After these there appeared a tumour on the upper part of the sternum like a large boil; by which appearance some vulgar surgeons being deceived, and either not having at all observed, or having neglected the pulsation, applied such things as are generally used to bring these tumours to suppuration, and these applications were of the most violent kind. As the tumour still increased others applied emollient medicines from which it seemed to them to be diminished. But it not only soon recovered its former magnitude but was . . . seen to increase every day.

"Wherefore, when the patient came into the Hospital of Incurables . . . it was equal in size to a quince and . . . began to exude blood in one place so that the man himself was very near having broken through the skin . . . when he began to pull off the bandages, for the sake of showing his disorder.

"But . . . he was prevented going on, and ordered to keep himself still, and to think seriously and piously of his departure from this mortal life, which was very near at hand and inevitable. And this really happened on the day following from the vast profusion of blood that had been foretold, though not so soon expected by the patient. Nevertheless, he had the presence of mind immediately as he felt the blood gushing forth, not only to commend himself to God, but to take up with his own hands a basin that lay at his bed-side, and, as if he had been receiving the blood of another person, put it beneath the gaping tumour."

THE CABOT CASE-RECORDS

Our panoramic sweep covers another century and a half and crosses an ocean to New England. There, in Boston, at the Massachusetts General Hospital, April, 1914, saw the commencement of an enterprise in the Morgagni mode and tradition—the Cabot Case Records.

The primary imaginative inspiration came from the brothers Cabot—Richard the physician and Hugh the surgeon. But week by week since their day the ante-mortem and post-mortem records of the hospital have been used to provide the dialectical and demonstration material for an inquisition, known throughout the world as the clinicopathological exercise or conference.

Approximately 5000 cases have been carried to a complete conclusion and elucidation at these conferences, and recorded accordingly. Only rarely has the arbiter, the pathologist, had to say *causa mortis ignota*. This M.G.H. collection is a thing unique in the modern medical world.

The original conferences were the private and somewhat informal arena of the Cabots and their students. Later, the circle of disputants was enlarged, and now each Thursday-morning conference has its own pair of prima donnas, sometimes from the resident company, sometimes guest artistes.

Comparisons between 1914, or even 1924, and the present day mark the tremendous increase in the armamentarium of diagnosis, a change in the types of disease encountered, and the rising level of the age of patients.

Only on a few diseases can one reasonably contrast the showing of the old warriors and the new.

For those who delight in such comparison I would recommend a study of the differential diagnosis of miliary tuberculosis. They will find that, despite the greater refinement of X-ray technique and the evolution of laboratory procedures which have aggrandised the electrolytes, the mother wit and experience of the clinician are often the deciding factors. And over the years the personal honours are evenly divided.

THE ESSENTIALS

It is time to gather together the lessons of our circumspection in time and place. Nearly 5000 years come within our compass, for the earliest Egyptian record precedes the Edwin Smith papyrus by a millennium. From their primitive salves, linen rolls, and incantations to our antibiotics and radioactive isotopes is a gigantic stride. Yet we still use salves and bandages, we still

place men at their mooring stakes. Now as always observation
and experience are the foundation upon which diagnosis, treatment, and prognosis are built. Individual men and women are
no less prone to error, and that fallibility is another of the
companionable common factors which help to bridge the ages.

From the point of view of the student of records, those treasures
which he rescues from the archives can never be better than
the best of the efforts of the best of the contemporary clinicians
and scientists.

One does not expect Mayerne to anticipate and outdo Morgagni. The trouble arises when the physician of the day falls
short of the Hippocratic standards, and uses the cant phrases of
the moment instead of his mother wits.

Let us see if we can distinguish some of the essentials of good
record-keeping as we have already observed them.

Above all comes the scheduling of the facts, and the little
verse of Kipling mentions most of them.

> "I keep six honest serving-men, (they taught me all I knew) Their names
> are What and Why and When, and How and Where and Who."

But in our studies we have been given more than facts. The
best records have been pictures, and the attributes of those
pictures have been these—at least as I see them.

Order has been a characteristic throughout. What more
orderly than the presentation of the Egyptian warrior's broken
nose, or the recital of the pathology of the living as seen in
James I.

Accuracy.—Here we have no yardsticks except we regard as
such our ability, despite the efflux of time, and the difficulties of
definitions and translations, to recognise the descriptions and the
diagnoses as comparable to something within our knowledge and
experience.

Brevity.—Except Mayerne, the writers of all our texts are
masters of concise expression. Morgagni is discursive at times,
but that is when he is bent on instructing his young friend.
When he wills it, no-one can epitomise more pertinently or more
epigrammatically. Then other less important virtues have been
disclosed—*Balance* in the presentation of a mass of information;
and *Saliency,* the gift of emphasising the outstanding features.

Finally, we come to *Selectivity*. Except for Mayerne—and his essay was on a special theme—all our teachers have been selective in the information they have laid before us. They have not invited us to study everything, but only certain examples from their several collections.

Hippocrates, in writing the Constitutions, obviously draws upon more clinical material than he leaves with us in the individual cases of the books of *Epidemics*. Morgagni, also tells that, if he were to write all that he knows about aneurysms, it would fill a volume in itself.

It seems impossible to contemplate the holding of a grand clinicopathological conference on every inguinal hernia or tonsillectomy. The essential facts must be recorded. The six honest serving-men must make their mark.

Thereafter, as with our predecessors, a wise discretion will determine what shall be set out in detail, and what omitted, for the guidance, instruction, and charitable consideration of posterity.

BIBLIOGRAPHY

Edwin Smith Surgical Papyrus, translated by H. Breasted. Chicago, 1930.

Hippocrates, translated by W. H. S. Jones. London, 1923; vol. I, pp. 202, 211.

Moore, N. Medicine in the British Isles. Oxford, 1908; pp. 97. et seq.

Morgagni, J. B. The Seats and Causes of Disease, translated by B. Alexander, M.D. London, 1769; vol. I, pp. 3, 796, 819; vol. III, p. 504.

READING AND WRITING

—————8—————

An Unusual Obstetrical Case History

Derived from the Pen of W. Shakespeare*

By Some Version of Meaning and
Extraction from Context

RICHARD D. BRYANT, M.D.

Each phrase or sentence of the following case history is a direct quotation from Shakespeare. The only words used which do not appear anywhere in Shakespeare are the following: Abdominal, anesthetist, manipulating, menstrual, October, obstetrical, ophthalmoscope, pelvic, stork.

This represents an unusual knowledge and love of the great Bard as well as a true and delightful sense of humor. That the author is a well informed obstetrician goes without saying. In the original unabridged manuscript, each phrase or sentence carries the Shakespearean source, both as to title, act, and scene. Unfortunately, space does not permit the publication of these as they appear in the complete and original paper, but the reader may rest assured as to their accuracy.

THE EDITOR

SYNOPSIS

DOLL TEARSHEET *visits* DR. PINCH, *who establishes a diagnosis of pregnancy. Difficulty is anticipated two months later when it is evident that complications are present. Long after these two prenatal visits,* DOLL *convulses. Labor is induced, but is unsatisfactory. Accouchement force fails, the uterus is ruptured, and laparotomy is resorted to. The postoperative course is somewhat stormy.*

The cast of characters, in order of their appearance, is as follows:

DR. PINCH, *a physician*
DOLL TEARSHEET, *a patient*

* Deceased.

Reprinted from OBSTETRICS AND GYNECOLOGY
Volume 2, pages 187–200, August, 1953

ASSISTANT, TO DR. PINCH
MALMSEY-BUTT TEARSHEET, *Doll's husband*
AN OFFICE NURSE
DR. CAIUS, *a physician*
PLACENTIO, *a midwife*
ORDERLY
A HOSPITAL NURSE
EXTERN
DR. SHAW, *a surgeon*
DR. MORPHEUS, *an anaesthetist*
DR. STORK, *an Ob-Gyn board man*

Any similarity of persons living or dead to members of the cast
of characters is inconceivable.

*It is mid-October. A lady
consults* DR. PINCH *in his
office*

DR. P.
Thy history fully unfold. What
is your name?

DOLL
Doll Tearsheet.

DR. P. (to assistant)
Where was she born?

ASS'T
Between Scylla and Charybdis.

DR. P.
Occupation

DOLL
Housewife.

DR. P.
Age?

DOLL
Some fifty, inclining to three
score.

DR. P.
Your marriage?

DOLL
Three months married.

DR. P.
Any more than one husband?

DOLL
Nine, sir; a widow to seven of
the nine.

DR. P.
Complaint?

DOLL
I'll tell thee my disease. I have
a young conception in my maid-
en's organ. I am sorry, but not
afeard. I am a fool to weep at
what I am glad of.

DR. P.
Menstrual history?

DOLL
A bloody period once in a
month from seventeen years till

now. Near twenty years ago, I did not flow for three months; often too late a week, sometimes a month's length apiece; a pretty period the tenth of August last; a period of twenty three days a month before. I stained this napkin Wednesday last. It is not that time of moon with me. I may miscarry?

DR. P.
A sad occasion if you miscarry?

DOLL
Why should I joy in an abortive birth?

DR. P.
Present illness?

DOLL
I am sick. Ten meals I have lost. I vomit green. Things sweet to taste prove in digestion sour. I belch from my heart. My gorge rises. My stomach is not constant. When I have stomach to eat I am heart-burned an hour after. My swelling dugs do ache. My nose fell a-bleeding. I have the toothache I fain would sleep a twelve-month and a day. I have longing for stewed prunes. I longed to eat adders' heads and toads carbonadoed. Up twenty times a night to the privy. I itch from head to foot. I wash, wring, brew, bake, scour, dress meat and drink, make the beds, and do all myself.

DR. P.
Past history?

DOLL
I came into the world with my legs forward. I am not such a sickly creature. In the calendar of my past I have a strange infirmity, which is nothing to those that know me—the falling sickness. My lungs are wasted in a consumption. I caught a burning quotidian tertian fever; had boils, full, all over, generally; a plague-sore, an embossed carbuncle; the gout, serpigo, and the rheum; profound heaves; the bone-ache; rheumatic fever; the green sickness; pleurisy; whooping cough; those measles; and piles; the rotten diseases of the south, the guts griping, ruptures, catarrhs, loads o' gravel i' the back, lethargies, cold palsies, raw eyes, dirt-rotten livers, wheezing lungs, bladders full of imposthume, sciaticas, limekilns i' the palm, incurable bone-ache, and the rivelled fee-simple of the tetter. I have been possessed with the glanders, and like to mose in the chine; troubled with the lampass, infected with the fashions, fell of wind-galls, sped with spavins, rayed with the yellows, past cure of the fives, stark spoiled with the staggers, begnawn with the bots,

swayed in the back, and shoulder-shotten; had a gangren'd appendix—there remains some scar of the operation. This ear is deaf.

DR. P.

As many diseases as two and fifty horses!

DOLL

Feed yourselves with questioning.

DR. P.

Family history?

DOLL

My mother, not fourteen, a young budding virgin, fair and fresh and sweet, grew round-wombed, and had indeed, sir, a son for her cradle ere she had a husband for her bed. Too soon marr'd are those so early made. I have twenty brothers. Twice when that my mother went with child, my father by true computation of the time, found that the issue was not his begot. In childbed died she. Father died this morning of a malignancy.

DR. P.

Obstetrical history?

DOLL

Well I conceive. Conception is a blessing. I have borne and borne and borne. My womb, my womb, my womb undoes me. I have three daughters; the eldest is eleven; the second and the third, nine and some five. The only son of my womb was from his mother's womb untimely ripp'd. He came into the world full fourteen weeks before the course of time—came something saucily into the world before he was sent for. There was good sport at his making, and the whoreson must be acknowledged. My male issue or died where they were made, or shortly after this world had air'd them, making their tomb the womb wherein they grew. My womb falls much lower than my knees. I miscarried by my fault a dozen times at least. A surgeon scraped one out of my womb. Two children at one birth four times, and a mother to the birth of three at once within ten years. I have borne children of divers kind and of strange shapes, one with two seeming bodies, but one heart.

DR. P.

Call thy husband hither.

Husband enters

What is your name?

M-B.

Malmsey-butt Tearsheet.

DOLL

To M-b.

With many holiday and lady terms he question'd me.

DR. P.

The question is concerning your marriage.

M-B.

She is able to freeze the god Priapus. I had rather to adopt a child than get it.

DR. P.

She disdains the tillage of thy husbandry?

M-B.

She's too rough for me.

DR. P.

A strange bull leap'd your cow, and got a calf in that same noble feat?

M-B.

She has been sluic'd. She is pregnant by a youth of fourteen (one would think his mother's milk were scarce out of him). Groping for trouts in a peculiar river, he plough'd her, and she cropp'd. It is a wise father that knows his own child. 'Tis partly mine own fault. I have heard it said the fittest time to corrupt a man's wife is when she's fallen out with her husband. She quickly pooped him.

DOLL

This momentary joy breeds months of pain. Almost at fainting under the pleasing punishment that women bear, a babe is moulded. Women grow by men—so they come by great bellies. It is a great price for a small vice. I thought with child, my master is become a hot lover.

M-B.

Let copulation thrive!

DR. P.

Some natural notes about her body.

To his assistant

What stature is she of?

ASS'T

No longer from head to foot than from hip to hip. This huge hill of flesh is spherical, like a globe. She is deformed, ill-fac'd, worse-bodied, shapeless everywhere, thick-sighted, barren, and lacking juice.

DR. P.

Take you the marks of her—the colour of her hair, complexion, height, age, with warrant of her virginity.

ASS'T

Inventoried—item, two lips indifferent red; item, two gray eyes with lids to them; item, one neck, one chin, and so forth, a hand, a foot, a face, an eye, a gait, a state, a brow, a breast, a waist, a leg, a limb; sides and heart; liver, brain; huge legs; lank and all o'er-teemed loins; on her left breast a mole cinque-spotted.

DOLL
I am very heavy.

DR. P.
You are well fleshed. Your bum is the greatest thing about you.

DOLL
I do here walk before thee like a sow.

DR. P.
How long is't ago since thou sawest thine own knee?

DOLL
These fifteen years.

Pelvic examination

DOLL
I am galled.

DR. P.
The quivering thigh, and the demesnes that there adjacent lie, the mons, the groin, art raw. The external parts with continual action are even as good as rotten, bare-gnawn and canker-bit. There are no venereal signs. 'Scutcheon female. You are wide betwixt the legs. It stretches from an inch narrow to an ell broad. A commodious drab. The passage, 'tis not as deep as a well, nor so wide as a church-door, but 'tis enough, 'twill serve. This cockpit seems a mile to the bottom.

DOLL
I am so dwarfish and so low, measure me.

DR. P.
Those parts of thee that the world's eye doth view are disproportioned. We'll measure her from hip to hip, the circumference, length and breadth, both high and low, posterior and in front.

Measures
A wide arch. Inferior and middle straits too narrow. The brim is not big enough, the diameter too short; ilium deep and broad to an unnatural degree. The promontory? I cannot reach so high.

To Doll
You are shallow, too flat, too short, and contracted, with bones at an odd angle.

DOLL
My dimensions are compact. There's a divinity that shapes our ends.

DR. P.
Her womb? O, 'tis pregnant, pregnant.

DOLL
How many months?

DR. P.
She is two months on her way.

To Doll
Thou art a difficult weight, a load would sink a navy.

DOLL
I am a huge feeder. I do noth-

ing but sit and sit, and eat and eat.

DR. P.
Be spare in diet. Eat no more than will preserve just so much strength.

DOLL
Who can cloy the hungry edge of appetite by bare imagination of a feast?

DR. P.
One day in a week touch no food, and but one meal on every day beside. If you feed upon such nice and waterish diet, the appetite may sicken and so die.

DOLL
I expressly am forbid to touch mustard?

DR. P.
It makes the hare-lip.

DOLL
I'll dine and sup with water and bran.

DR. P.
I care not what, so it be wholesome food. Leave gormandizing, know the grave doth gape for thee thrice wider than for the lean and hungry.

DOLL
No pullet-sperm in my brewage? fat tripe? toasted cheese?

DR. P.
Dainty bits make rich the ribs.

Living dully sluggardized at home, thou art inclin'd to sleep? Walk in the park!

DOLL
'Twill do me good to walk. Is there no quick recreation granted? Allow me exercises.

DR. P.
If it be not too rough, little but bowling, tennis, swimming, wrestling, and dice.

DOLL
Liquor?

DR. P.
Two glasses Fridays and Saturdays.

DOLL
Smoke?

DR. P.
A pack in fourteen days. Also, one of these maids' girdles for your waist should befit.

DOLL
An austere insociable life!

The twelfth day of December; Doll visits Dr. P.

DR. P.
Since I saw you last there is a change upon you.

ASS'T
The fair soul herself weigh'd she gained a hundred pounds.

DOLL
I am in the waist two yards about—like great-bellied wom-

en, that have not half a week
to go.

DR. P.

False reckonings?

DOLL

Honourable reckoning.

ASS'T

She is spread of late into a
goodly bulk. The child brags
in her belly already. She feels
her young one kick.

DR. P.

Too much of water hast thou.
There's something extraordinary in thee.

DOLL

Believe me, there's no such
thing in me. Pendulous-bel-
lied, no supporter can hold
it up. I pray God my girdle
break. I sleep but three hours
in the night. I have caught
extreme cold, foregone all exercises. My panting bulk, 'tis
very pregnant. Four days ago
a tooth-drawer pulled out a
raging tooth, for there was
never yet philosopher that
could endure the toothache patiently. What says the doctor to
my water?

ASS'T

He said the water itself was a
good healthy water; but, for the
party that owned it, she might
have more diseases than she
knew of.

DR. P.

You must come in earlier
o'nights, henceforth eat no fish
or salt-butter. Fast a week with
bran and water and a dish of
skimmed milk.

As she leaves

ASS'T

The belching whale! That
trunk of humours, that bolting-
hutch of beastliness, that swollen parcel of dropsies, that huge
bombard of sack, that stuffed
cloak-bag of guts!

NURSE

She that makes dainty, she, I'll
swear hath corns!

DR. P.

A gentle lady, big of this gentleman—there is no lady of more
softer bowels!

*The first of May. Malmsey-
butt appears frantically at
Dr.'s house*

M-B.

Doll is fallen into an epilepsy!
Some fit or frenzy do possess
her with dry convulsions!

*Dr. and Ass't go with M-b.
and examine Doll, who is
again conscious*

DR. P.

In thy face strange motions
have appear'd, such as we see

when men restrain their breath on some great sudden hest.

Ass't takes blood pressure
There is high blood pressure?

ASS'T
Two hundred and fifty over a hundred and fifty.

DR. P.
Let me see your eyes with my ingenious instrument.

Examine with ophthalmos-cope
Each petty artery contracted. The urine is congealed by vinegar and boiling. Your head did but ache?

DOLL
I have a pain upon my forehead here. Winking, there appears quick-shifting antics, ugly in my eyes.

DR. P.
Such shadows are the weak brain's forgeries.

DOLL
His face seems twain, each several limb is doubled. Everything seems double. Around night's candles many-coloured rings.

DR. P.
Oft the eye mistakes, the brain being troubled.

DOLL
Lord, how my head aches! It beats as it would fall in twenty pieces. My sight fails.

Speaking thick
I am, on the sudden, something ill.

Falls in a trance; the fit is momentary

DR. P.
The disease is violent. The lethargy must have his quiet course; if not, it by and by breaks out to savage madness. She hath kept an evil diet long, and overmuch consumed. 'Tis perturbation of the brain—brain-sick fits.

M-B.
The nature of the disease found, what is the remedy?

R. P.
To cure it, easy. The most sovereign prescription in Galen is but empiricutic, but in these cases some prescriptions of rare and prov'd effects—the blest infusions that dwell in vegetives, in metals, stones—are superior to newfound methods and to compounds strange—a pure compound of lily-tincture, a noted weed like to aconitum, between eight and nine drops by needle here in the thigh; also purgative salt in the hip.

To Doll
Patiently receive my medicine. The salt in thy diet hath made thee swell thus. Salt little.

DOLL

I had rather fast.

Next day

DOLL

I loathe this food, and felt more than a mother's pain from that poisoned shot.

DR. P.

I dare not delay till your date expire. We must induce your labour by the rupture of your water.

DOLL

Things growing are not ripe until their season.

DR. P.

In this time of lethargy 'twere well it were done quickly.

Manipulating

I am making a little hole in your bag of waters.

From her most miraculous organ full of water, downward flowed apace a wide sea of brine for twenty watchful, weary, tedious nights. There is some show but she feels no pain

DR. P.

We will proceed no further in this business. We need Dr. Caius, the renowned French physician that have the office opposite to mine.

M-B.

I will bring the doctor.

Goes to his house

DR. C.

I have not been in bed tonight. Faintness constraineth me to measure out my length on this cold bed.

M-B.

'Tis too late to go to bed now.

Dr. C. goes to M-b.'s home. It is early Saturday morning

DR. C.

What's the matter?

DR. P.

I will a round unvarnish'd tale deliver.

Relates the case

DR. C.

I have been in such a pickle. I wonder at this haste. There's no harm done. I will do what I can. We may effect this business yet ere day. Let's consult together.

He inward search'd Doll

A bag—that's the appliance only which your disease requires.

DR. P.

That is an old device.

An old woman arrives

Here's Placentio, the midwife.

Dr. C. inserts bag

DR. C.

By six o'clock tonight thou shalt have cramps, sidestitches that shall pen thy breath up. By eleven o'clock it will go one way or other. Patient expectation!

> *Betwixt twelve and one Sunday morning Doll was taken with the cramp and pinched with the colic*

MDWF.

'Tis now your labour. Very little pains will bring this labour to an happy end.

DOLL

Give me nothing for my labour. The labour we delight in physics pain. Shall I be appointed hours? If not tonight, why, then, tomorrow night; or Tuesday morn; on Tuesday noon, or night; on Wednesday morn— I pr'ythee name the time; but let it not exceed three days. Midwife gentle, make swift the pangs of my travail. Vouchsafe my labour. This is most certain that I'll deliver myself. Sweet thoughts do even refresh my labours.

> *Later*

Hell-pains! Painful labour, effect one thing specially!

MDWF.

Perchance you think too much of so much pains.

DOLL

Time travels in divers paces with divers persons.

MDWF.

Be not frantic. Nature is thy friend.

DOLL

I will no longer endure it. Pr'ythee a shot of poppy. My poor body, madam, requires it.

MDWF.

> *Giving a shot*

Take this for thy pains.

DOLL

> *Later*

It did relieve me. For this relief, much thanks. How long shall I be patient? Is there more toil?

MDWF.

Now is your time.

> *Doll bears down. To herself*

In peril of precipitation!

> *Mdwf. goes to the next room to report to the Dr.*

DR. P.

Is she crying out?

MDWF.

Precipitating! Sweating, and blowing, and looking wildly, and would needs speak with you presently; desperate, with her nails her flesh doth tear.

DR. P.

Neigh, and bark, and grunt, and roar! A plague upon this howling!

MDWF.
To herself
The patient dies while the physician sleeps!
Dr. P. goes to see patient

DR. P.
Where lies thy pain?

DOLL
My back o' t'other side—Oh, my back, my back! One minute, nay, one quiet breath of rest! My little body is hot, faint, and weary. Heaven have mercy on me!

DR. P.
Shut your mouth, dame! Be patient!

DOLL
Do you not know I am a woman? When I think, I must speak. Immediate are my needs; and my relief must not be toss'd and turn'd to me in words, but find supply immediate. If ever man were mov'd with woman's moans, be moved with my tears, my sighs, my groans. It easeth some, though none it ever cur'd, to think their dolour others have endur'd.

DR. P.
The lady protests too much.

DOLL
It's monstrous labour! Pray you, you, sir, deliver me, lest with my sighs or tears I blast or drown the fruit within my womb. Give me a gash, put me to present pain.

DR. P.
To Midwf.
A wretched soul, bruis'd with adversity, we bid be quiet when we hear it cry; but were we burden'd with like weight of pain, as much, or more, we should ourselves complain.
To Doll
After you have laboured so hard to dilate at full, you shall be immediately deliver'd.
Examines by most mechanical and dirty hand

DR. P.
To himself
Three fingers dilated.
Takes bag out
Brow? The skull is moulded. I can do not hurt to try conversion. The body of contraction hurts my hand.

MDWF.
Then belike your hand is in.

DR. P.
Some monster with four legs. I'll pull thee by the lesser legs.
Pulls
He's irremovable. I had rather have it a head.

MDWF.
Go on and turn again.

DR. P.

What a coil's here—the cord.
Let me cut his thread of life.
Cuts
Let us have the tongs.
They put on their instruments—forged hooks, fearful hooks. The bloody steel grasp'd the crown. It did not budge.

To Doll

It is a common thing. Let me clip you. I must be cruel only to be kind.

DOLL

May you prove, sir, master of your art.

DR. P.

I have killed none so. Let us make incision i' the neck of thy womb. I had rather cut a little with my knife than tear her all to pieces.
Cuts, ripping up the womb, that inward breaks

MDWF.

Are not these large enough?

DR. P.

Too deep incision, too long by half a mile.
The inch-thick sever'd lips on both sides drizzled blood. Dr. doth backward pull, 'gainst nature still.

MDWF.

Not so hot!
She bleeds. The crimson blood circles her body in on every side, came pouring, like the tide into a breach, like a fountain with a hundred spouts, as if those organs had deceptious functions created only to calumniate

DR. P.

To Doll

I will modestly discover to yourself that of yourself which you yet know not of. I have killed the issue of your womb. Thou bleed'st too much. We beslubber our garments with it!

DOLL

Women are valiant. My firm nerves shall never tremble. Things without all remedy should be without regard: What's done is done.

DR. P.

To Mdwf.

What shall I do?

MDWF.

Diseases desparate grown by desparate appliances are reliev'd. Cannot you and I perform an operation? I'll thy assistant be. We must do something. The cause craves haste.

DR. P.

I have no skill in surgery.

MDWF.

To herself

He has not skill enough to deliver a fly from a spider.

DR. P.
This disease is beyond my practice.

MDWF.
Then let her alone.

DR. P.
Dispose of her to some more fitter place; and that with speed.
To Doll
Your doctors hold it very meet that you may be conveniently delivered in a hospital.

They move Doll to the hospital

Nurse appears

NURSE
To Doll
Get on your nightgown. Move her to the labourer's room.

DOLL
Some blessed power deliver us. I beseech your grace that I may know the worst that may befall me in this case.
Extern appears

EXT.
What bloody business! What's her history?

DOLL
I am not well. I was hither brought with child, at term. All swoln, I had fits. Physicians forc'd those waters from me which I would have stopp'd. I labour'd much, was cut but not deliver'd, so this was the most unkindest cut of all. I bleed apace and shed my dear blood drop by drop.

EXT.
Let me check thee.
To himself
Why should nature build so foul a den? A very fatal place it seems to me. It hath no bottom. No water thence proceeds, the parts extremely stretched. The head is now high, the sticking place is of most narrow measure. It will not come down tonight, not an inch further. Only three fingers dilated. She is white as a lily, whiter than the sheets.
To Doll
You look paler and paler. Why is your cheek so pale?

DOLL
I bleed inwardly, and was o'er shoes in blood.*

EXT.
To himself
The jerks! This punk hath a license?

DR. P.
Here's packing.

EXT.
You bid me pack?
To himself
It is a judgment maim'd and most imperfect.

* Parks' sign?—ED.

To Dr.
She may not endure hazard so
dangerous as doth hourly grow.
Go; fetch a surgeon! Go with
all speed to Dr. Shaw.
          Dr. Shaw is brought in
DR. S.
I will not cast away my physic
but on those that are sick.
          Examines her
Fever has bak'd thy blood and
made it heavy, which else runs
tickling up and down the veins.
DOLL
So much blood thither came,
have I not reason to look pale
and dead?
DR. S.
'Tis a condition that nothing
can allay, nothing but blood,
infused in thy cold and empty
veins, where no blood dwells.
EXT.
          To Doll
I must have an ounce or two of
blood from you for the test.
DOLL
There's the vein.
          Extern draws blood
EXT.
          After typing, to Shaw
A half pint of blood?
DR. S.
Quarts!
          *Infusion of blood is com-
          pleted*

DR. S.
Notwithstanding all this loss of
blood—as from a conduit with
three issuing spouts—yet do thy
cheeks look red as Titan's face.
Blood hath the victory!
          Doll is taken to X-ray
My master sends you for a picture with this machine that
through thy bosom makes me
see thy heart.
          Pictures are taken
DOLL
Was ever man so rayed?
          *Shaw and extern examine
          pictures*
DR. S.
Three infants—a three-headed
monster with four legs, com-
passed in the circumference of
a peck, hilt to point, heel to
head; and twins. I have operations in my head.
DOLL
Knife, drug, operation! I'll
make my will then!
          *Doll is put on operating
          table*
It is like a barber's chair, that
fits all buttocks—the pin-but-
tock, the quatch-buttock, the
brawn-buttock, or any buttock.
My bones would rest, that have
but labour'd to attain this hour.
Grant that I might sleep out
this great gap of time.
          *Dr. Morpheus, the anesthe-
          tist, appears*

DR. M.

I'll medicine thee to that sweet sleep with vapours and drowsy syrups. I would not have thee linger in thy pain.

Puts mask over her nose
Smell somewhat strong? You need not stop your nose, nor hold hard the breath. Therefore exhale, pant! Through all thy veins shall run a cold and drowsy humor; for no pulse shall keep his native progress, but surcease; no warmth, no breath, shall testify thou liv'st; the roses in thy lips and cheeks shall fade to paly ashes; thy eyes' windows fall, like death, when he shuts up the day of life; each part, depriv'd of supple government, shall, stiff and stark and cold, appear like death: and in this borrow'd likeness of shrunk death thou shalt continue two-and-forty hours, and then awake as from a pleasant sleep. There is no danger in what show of death it makes, more than the locking up the spirits a time, to be more fresh, reviving, 'Twill cease the present power of life; but in short time all offices of nature should again do their due functions.

DOLL

Why does my blood thus muster to my heart, making it both un-able for itself and dispossessing all the other parts of necessary fitness? It makes me have a slow heart.

DR. M.
Soon sleep in quiet.
Shortly
Half asleep—she dost snore distinctly.
Shortly
What, all so soon asleep?

DR. S.
I'll make some hole through which I may convey these babes, a two-fold operation, Caesar's operation, by us performed before. Mask for faces and for noses! Pare thy nails! wash your hands! Powder, gloves, sterile gown. Knife, tape, shears! With this obedient steel, three inches of it, with instruments fit, I make incision in thee.
The needle his finger pricks
From my forehead wipe sweat! A pox! I prick your guts a little.
Snip, and nip, and cut, and slish, and slash, and even spit in the hole
One mess! The despair of surgery! Past all surgery!
Dropped his knife
Some Dick knows the trick. Send for the surgeon midwife, Dr. Stork—a learned doctor, his active practice in these specialties. He can carve, too, more es-

pecially when our most learned doctors leave us, and the congregated college have concluded that labouring art can never ransom nature from her inaidable estate. He would have us live and study here three years, where none will sweat but for promotion.

Doll goes into intestine shock.

I say she's dead! Seek the coroner!

DR. M.
Her pulse beats. She will recover.

Morpheus wrings her nose, he strikes her on the cheeks, he bends her fingers, holds her pulse hard; he chafes her lips, a thousand ways he seeks to mend

DR. M.
The ocular proof—lend me a looking-glass; if her breath will mist or stain the stone, why, then she lives. Death may usurp on nature many hours, and yet the fire of life kindle again the o'erpress'd spirits. Just against her heart make thou a hole, and give a shot of restoratives.

Shaw wakes her heart by beating on her breast

I think she lives.

Stork arrives

DR. S.
This is desparate, sir.

STORK
What particular rarity? what strange, which manifold record not matches? Conjecture, expectation, and surmise of aids uncertain, should not be admited.

DR. S.
She hath not been entranc'd above five hours.

STORK
She was splitted in the midst, unseam'd from the nave to the chaps?

DR. S.
Was't not the way? I have a wound here that was like a T, but now 'tis made an H.

STORK
A perilous gash. This is the silliest stuff that ever I heard!

To Doll, although asleep
Are you not hurt i' the groin? Me-thought he made a shrewd thrust at your belly.

To Shaw
It is a rupture of the womb, which all this while had bled. In this case, then we shall repent each drop of blood that hot rash haste so indirectly shed. You have been a boggler ever. This is but a butchery.

To nurse
Omit nothing may give us aid.

To extern
I entreat you wear your gloves. Put on this gown. Come hither

mask'd. Take you your instrument. Lay the finger thus. Do cut but deep enough. Not too fast, nor cut thou less nor more. Your knife was dull and blunt. My reputation is at stake. Give me an instrument. Lights, more lights! Exposure! All the organs are black and blue. I will bring this monstrous birth.

Operates, bringing forth parts of one of the rarer monsters, three-headed and too hideous to be shown, and male twins, both alike.

To Shaw

Trim her up. Solder up the rift. Leave no rubs nor botches.

Removes gown and gloves and later returns to the table

Still a-repairing? A midwife could have better sew'd than thou. What are you sewing here?

DR. S.

Spleen, liver, the liver vein, intestine, bladder, gall bladder and womb.

STORK

O hell. Ply thy needle. Your stitchery is not so hot. Look you the knots be strong.

As the abdominal wall is closed

And thus she is delivered! It is a miracle!

Doll wakes

DOLL

I have been long a sleeper.

DR. S.

From forth the kennel of thy womb hath crept a hell-hound.

DOLL

I am sham'd by that which I bring forth.

STORK

You also became a joyful mother of two goodly sons. 'Twas a rough night. Give me some aqua vitae.

DR. S.

I have yet room for six scotches more.

The infants, mewling and puking in the nurse's arm, are shown to Doll

DOLL

Are there balance here to weigh? A little tiny boy! A naked newborn babe! A purple-colour'd face? Give it breath with your mouth! Never mole, hare-lip, nor scar. Sans teeth, sans eyes, sans taste, sans everything! A little wee face. 'Tis dimpled! The prettiest babe that e'er I delivered. Mark it well in the cradle where it lies. Dress it in cradle clothes, a diaper, booties, The other very pale, the jaundice on your cheeks. Different in blood? Yet had I four negatives. Strange is it that our bloods, of colour,

weight, and heat, pour'd all together, would quite confound
distinction, yet stand off in differences so mighty. Drain the
life-blood of the child and in-
fuse new blood!

First post-operative day

DOLL
I have passed a miserable night.

NURSE
Last night she slept not.

DOLL
I would not so much as make
water, only dribbling.

DR. S.
Examining
A lump like a bladder—some
retention.

DOLL
A chilling sweat o'er-runs my
trembling joints.

NURSE
She is plagued with cramps,
and gouts, and painful fits.

Third post-operative day

NURSE
She is with a kind of colic
pinch'd and vex'd by the im-
prisoning of unruly wind within her womb. The afterloss
from the womb smells to heaven
—an odoriferous stench.

DR. S.
Thou art infected with the bug
of child-bed fever.

Examines wound
A foul expulsion on the dress-
ings. Thy cicatrice looks raw
and red, swoln and hot and
moist. 'Tis full of matter.

Fifth post-operative day

DR. S.
You have a lean cheek; a blue
eye and sunken. Let me feel
your pulse. Still no stool? I
pr'ythee take the cork out.

*Seventh day post-operative.
The bonds are slipp'd, dis-
sol'd, and loos'd, and the
wounds open their con-
geal'd mouths and bleed
afresh. The bowels sud-
denly burst out in a great
coil. Doll pants and looks
pale*

DR. S.
You look grim as hell!
*His repair is with wire.
He orders a thousand
grains of the golden quint-
essence of the honour'd
mould*

Eighth post-operative day

DR. S.
Take thy physic.

DOLL
Rhubarb, senna, or what purgative?

DR. S.
It is compounded of many sim-

ples. I know my physic will work. Thou art not quickly moved!

Ninth post-operative day

DOLL

Roaring for a chamber-pot

I shall break my wind!

NURSE

Later

An earthquake! A fuller blast ne'er shook our wards. She is most potent in potting.

DOLL

I have passed a three-foot stool. Now can I break my fast, dine, sup, and sleep.

Twelfth post-operative day

DOLL

I am not well today. My ankles swell so much.

DR. S.

It is coagulate gore in the blood vessel of your leg. Lie straight in bed. No more moving. Talk not of standing. I fear too much rubbing of the calf muscles, lest congealed blood retrograde to the lungs and you die suddenly.

DOLL

I'll stay a month longer.

DR. S.

'Till thy wound be thoroughly heal'd.

Fortieth post-operative day

DR. S.

After two days I will discharge thee. A terrible childbed hast thou had.

DOLL

How light and portable my pain seems now, not remembering how I cried out then. It is worth the pains. My skin hangs about me like an old lady's loose gown. Look how well my garments sit upon me; much feater than before. I here forget all former griefs. Nature should produce without sweat or endeavour. Thy fee is a thousand ducats?

DR. S.

Dost thou forget from what a torment I did free thee? 'Tis too little payment for so great a debt.

DOLL

Will you take eggs for money?

Writes a countercheck

Keep that check for it.

DR. S.

Then I am paid.

DOLL

Do not look for further recompense. We can afford no more at such a price!

9

Teachers of Medicine

W. BARRY WOOD, JR., M.D.

TODAY WE CELEBRATE the twenty-fifth anniversary of the Central Society. The story of its genesis has been clearly set forth in print by the first secretary, Dr. Lawrence Thompson. To him and to the other founders, who guided the Society's early destiny, we are deeply indebted.

The chief objective of the Central Society has been to stimulate clinical research. During the past twenty-five years, it has continued to grow in stature, until in 1952 it ranks among leading medical societies of the country. Into its membership has come a steady stream of promising investigators. Their research endeavors in the laboratory and clinic have contributed significantly to the advancement of medicine. But besides being investigators, most of the members of the Central Society have also been clinical teachers. As a group they have exerted a profound influence upon medical education in the Middle West. For this reason, and because medical education is today under fire from a number of directions, I should like to devote my few remarks, not to clinical investigation, but to the teaching of medicine.

The task of the teacher has, during the lifetime of the Central Society, been drastically changed by the progress of science. To illustrate, I should like to cite a single example. One year before the Society was founded, the W. B. Saunders Company published the first edition of Cecil's *Textbook of Medicine*. The section on anemia in this first edition admirably summarizes the subject as taught to students in 1927. But in contrast to the 1951 edition, the presentation contains no reference to any of the

Presidential address, Twenty-fifth Annual Meeting of the Central Society for Clinical Research, Chicago, Ill., Nov. 7 and 8, 1952.

Reprinted from THE JOURNAL OF LABORATORY AND CLINICAL MEDICINE, Volume 41, pages 6–10, January, 1953.

following topics: erythroblastosis fetalis; Rh antibodies; abnormal hemoglobins of sickle-cell disease; aplastic crises of congenital hemolytic icterus; normal survival of red blood cells; thalassemia major and minor; paroxysmal nocturnal hemoglobinuria; Coombs' test; extrinsic and intrinsic factors; vitamin B_{12} therapy; pteroylglutamic acid; bone marrow aspiration; absorption and excretion of iron; and pathogenesis of anemia in sprue.

Though not necessarily complete, this list is long enough to indicate that the factual information available concerning anemia has substantially increased since 1927. And all of these new facts must be taught to medical students! Innumerable similar examples could be cited to illustrate the growth of knowledge which has swelled the medical curriculum to the bursting point and has immeasurably increased the complexities of teaching.

As the task of the teacher has grown more difficult, his critics have become more vociferous. Today he is accused of being so absorbed in the scientific advances of his subject that he has lost sight of the very objective of his calling—the training of physicians. He is said to have forgotten the art of bedside diagnosis, to have become dependent upon intricate and expensive laboratory tests and to have lost interest in the training of general practitioners. He is censured for ignoring the "patient as a whole" and for slighting the social and psychologic aspects of disease.

Because of these alleged deficiencies certain medical educators, materially aided by a number of foundations, have recently launched a vigorous campaign to reform medical education. They have recommended the introduction of home care programs and undergraduate preceptorships in general practice in order to provide more instruction in the practicalities of medicine. They have suggested the teaching of social sciences in medical school. They have called for more instruction in psychiatry in order to develop in medical students a deeper understanding of the whole person.

Let us examine for a moment these criticisms and suggested remedies.

As to the training of general practitioners, it cannot be denied that there is a need for versatile doctors in isolated communities. Although improvements in transportation have brought rural areas far closer in time to the nearest medical centers, there are still many regions of the country where the needs of the population require the services of general practitioners. With those who recommend more appropriate *postgraduate* training for general practice I have no quarrel. A limited number of internships and residencies designed specifically to prepare physicians to serve in rural communities seems justified. But to introduce such training into the undergraduate curriculum is an entirely different matter.

My disagreement with those who advocate the teaching of general practice in medical schools does not relate to the *need* for general practitioners, but rather to the suggestion that general practice should be taught at all to undergraduates. Surely no one will deny that the unprecedented progress in medicine during the past fifty years has come primarily from the advances of medical science translated into practice through medical education. The volume of basic knowledge which must be mastered by the medical students of today is far greater than ever before. And yet, we are now urged to teach students less about the science of medicine and more about the practical aspects of home care and office practice. Why, may I ask, should the undergraduate curriculum be any different for a general practitioner than for a neurosurgeon? Do they not both have to know a maximum of medical science? Can they, for example, give proper care to their anemic patients if they know nothing of Rh antibodies or the basic principles of iron metabolism?

Many who are not directly involved in the day-to-day teaching of medical students quickly forget that the most effective instruction in medicine is that which involves basic principles rather than practical facts. "For it is," to quote Barzun,[1] "the oldest fallacy about schooling to suppose that it can train a man for 'practical life.' Inevitably while the plan of study is being taught, 'practical life' has moved on." No thoughtful physician needs to be reminded that what was practical yesterday may be obsolete tomorrow. In contrast, basic principles in medicine are relatively stable. New ones are added from time to time and old ones are occasionally discarded, but the turnover is comparatively slow. Only knowledge based upon principles is sufficiently enduring to aid the modern doctor in his endless task of keeping pace with medicine. In short, general practice should have no more place in the undergraduate curriculum than should the practice of internal medicine or any other kind of practice. Changes in the medical curriculum, which sacrifice training in basic science, either preclinical or clinical, for practical experience, will inevitably lead to inferior medical care.

The real objective of undergraduate instruction is ably stated in the following quotation from a lecture recently published in the *British Medical Journal*.[2] "The student can scarcely be expected to realize what some of his teachers may forget, that when he qualifies it is not so much what he knows that matters as how well fitted he is to learn by his subsequent experience, and how well equipped he is to sift and assimilate the new diagnostic and therapeutic advances which will certainly come during his practicing lifetime. It may once have been true that the practice of medicine did not greatly change between qualification and retirement, but nothing could be further from the truth now. The student who qualified twenty years ago has since had to learn a great deal to remain even tolerably efficient. Of course there are aids to this necessary postgraduate learning, but the doctor must have a fairly well-developed capacity for critical thought and judgment. It is this capacity to examine critically new ideas, to select those worth while, and to incorporate them in the body of his knowledge which alone justifies the claim of the doctor to be a member of one of the learned professions."

To come to the second major criticism of present-day medical education, let us consider briefly the proper place of psychosomatic medicine in the undergraduate curriculum. Here I am quite willing to admit that as clinical teachers we frequently fail to lay adequate stress upon the psychological aspects of illness. Our shortcomings in this respect seem to stem primarily from two sources.

First, many of us have fallen far behind in our understanding of psychosomatic medicine. Too much in this field has seemed to us in the past to have been based upon flimsy evidence, or no evidence at all. As a result, we have tended to refer all problems of the psyche to the psychiatrist, or have merely ignored them altogether. Such a position is no longer tenable.

Research from the clinics of Wolff and Romano, for example, have been yielding for at least a decade concepts based upon as clear scientific evidence as those of any other branch of clinical medicine. To deny the importance of psychological factors in such diseases as bronchial asthma, ulcerative colitis, peptic ulcer, hypertension, and urticaria, to mention but a few, is to play the ostrich and bury our heads in the familiar sands of purely somatic reasoning.

But the solution to the problem does not lie in the training of more psychiatrists nor in the establishment of new departments of psychosomatic medicine. The subject matter belongs in internal medicine, pediatrics, surgery, and obstetrics, and it must be so taught to medical students. Foundations supporting developments in this field have erred in insisting upon the establishment of separate "departments" or "divisions" of psychosomatic medicine. The inevitable degree of autonomy thus created makes for easier bookkeeping, but at the same time tends to defeat the main objective of the program. How much more would be accomplished if psychosomatic experts were "planted" in the already existing departments, experts who would function as clinicians and not merely as consulting "psychosomaticists." We must have such colleagues in our very midst, as we now have experts in cardiology, metabolism, hematology, and the other sub-specialties of medicine, if we are ever to convince undergraduate students that this important field belongs in everyday clinical practice.

The second factor which makes the teaching of psychosomatic medicine so difficult is that of time. Accurate appraisal of the psychological aspects of a given patient's illness depends primarily upon the anamnesis, which, when properly taken, is to the physician by far the most time-consuming part of the examination. It must include adequate personal and social histories, and these require even more of the doctor's time than the conventional system review and present illness. If he is to treat the "patient as a whole," the physician must know "the patient as a whole." To do so, he must devote to each case not minutes but hours. As long as doctors are chronically rushed, the majority will fail to practice "comprehensive medicine."

Does it follow that "comprehensive medicine" should not be

taught to undergraduates? Certainly one of the main functions of medical schools is to foster change that will raise the standards of medical care. As teachers we can do much to encourage the physicians of the future to adopt a more comprehensive approach to the study and treatment of disease. In so doing, however, we, too, will be limited by time. To teach comprehensively, we shall have to see fewer patients with our students on ward rounds, and assign to them fewer cases in the clinic. We shall have to sacrifice volume for completeness. Such a trend has already been forced upon us by the technical advances of laboratory medicine. Since most major errors of clinical practice result from sins of omission, and since physicians all too readily learn to cut corners after finishing their formal training, I am convinced that a sacrifice of volume for completeness is pedagogically sound.

Finally, I should like to refer to the most serious problem of all in medical education; namely, that created by increasing specialization. An inevitable result of advancing knowledge, specialization today is exerting a powerful disrupting force upon all of higher education. To meet the problem in medicine particularly will require much wisdom, for outside pressures which exaggerate the difficulty are constantly increasing. Special groups are clamoring for more time in the curriculum. Funds are being made available through Congress for substantial support of special areas. Medical specialists through both local and nationwide drives are obtaining vast amounts of money from the public to further special projects. Even foundations, attempting to create better balance in medical education, are providing temporary support for what they consider to be neglected specialties.

I have referred advisedly to these forces as "outside pressures," for those who control their direction are, for the most part, men whose daily work has divorced them from the undergraduate teaching of medicine. The sensory end organ of the medical school most responsive to these pressures is "the administration," which likewise is often so burdened with other responsibilities as to have no time for teaching. This combination, which threatens to control the policies of medical schools, bypasses the teachers of medicine. It has already shown itself to be much too willing to mortgage the future, in order merely to meet the public pressures of the moment. If medical education is to continue to flourish, the *educational* policies of medical schools must remain in the hands of faculties and not of professional administrators. Only teachers devoting their lives to the core of learning are close enough to the complex problems of their profession to plan wisely the education of the future.

Whether or not society will continue to allow teachers of medicine to guide the destinies of medical schools will depend primarily upon our performance as educators. Dedicated to "the maintenance of balance between the advancement of knowledge and its consolidation,"[3] we must somehow find means of consolidating the deluge of new facts to be taught to our students. We must neutralize the centrifugal force of specialization. Under no circumstances must we permit the availability of project funds to determine our decisions of educational policy. Those of us in clinical practice must donate from busy days not only the necessary hours for teaching, but also enough additional time to keep sufficiently abreast of medical progress to remain properly qualified as teachers. Those of us on "full time" must refrain from using our university appointments solely "to boil the pot of individual research." Outside duties which take us away from our institutions must not be allowed to cut too deeply into undergraduate instruction. Those of us who by preference would limit our efforts solely to postgraduate teaching must also participate in the undergraduate program. In fact, all of us as faculty members must continually be reminded of our obligation to teach medical students. For upon the qualifications of those whom we graduate will depend the future of American medicine.

REFERENCES

1. Barzun, J.: Teacher in America, 1945, Little, Brown and Co.
2. Jones, A. Morgan: Medical Progress and Medical Education, Brit. M. J. 2: 466, 1952.
3. Clark, W. M.: A Challenge to Scholarship. University of Pennsylvania Bicentennial Congress, Philadelphia, 1941, University of Pennsylvania Press.

10

Medical Stamps

NOAH D. FABRICANT, M.D.

IN 1947 THE Post Office Department of the United States issued a three cent stamp, reproducing Samuel Luke Fildes' "The Doctor," to commemorate the work of physicians as part of the celebration of the birth of the American Medical Association 100 years before. Recognition at this time of the physician's role in society, at least postagewise, was due in great measure to the growing awareness in many countries that medical men, medical events, and medical institutions are often fully as important as kings, queens, presidents, dictators, and generals. Actually, the number of postage stamps now commemorating medical and allied scientific achievements is so large that even the most ardent collector may be startled by the proportions of the field of medical philately. Because it is so extensive only a few aspects can be touched on in this article.

Sooner or later medical philately, if its pursuit is not to be haphazard and superficial, requires of the hobbyist a knowledge of medical history. The reason for this is that medical philately deals not only with medical portraiture, medical events, and medical mythology but also with medical buildings and institutions, stamps depicting diseases and medical botany, the Caduceus, the Red Cross, and Health Postal Taxes. In reality, there is much room for specialization in medical philately as there is in the practice of medicine. For beginners a collection of medical portraits is probably the easiest to acquire, since many physicians have been commemorated both for their work in medicine and for their contributions and achievements in nonmedical fields.

There seems to have been no planned trend in the use of physicians' heads on postage stamps. In 1928, a famous physician's features greeted the addressee of almost every letter from Holland. The features were those of Hermann Boerhaave, who

Reprinted from JOURNAL OF THE AMERICAN MEDICAL ASSOCIATION
Vol. 152, p. 1364–1365, August 1, 1953.

was born in 1668, and who became the first great clinical or "bedside" teacher. Until the 17th century there had been no systematic
clinical teaching and all of the universities conferred medical
degrees on the basis of a spoken disputation. Contact with
patients was not required of medical novitiates and practitioners
until Boerhaave instituted clinical teaching in 1701. In 1935
the Netherlands issued a six cent stamp depicting Frans Cornelis
Donder, the famous Dutch ophthalmologist who was a notable
contributor to physiological optics during the past century, introducing the use of prismatic and cylindrical lenses for the correction of certain types of eye defects and offering the first exact
definitions of myopia and presbyopia.

In 1937 Austria paid homage to the old Vienna School of
Medicine by placing the portraits of nine famous 19th century
physicians on a series of stamps. These included Theodor Billroth,
who was the founder of modern visceral surgery; Karl von Rokit-
ansky, who performed more than 30,000 autopsies during his
lifetime and who made voluminous contributions to the field of
pathology; Ferdinand von Hebra, founder of the histological
school of dermatology; Leopold Auenbrugger, discoverer of percussion as a diagnostic procedure; Joseph Skoda, whose name is
given to the rale found in pneumonia; Carl Ferdinand von
Arlt, whose treatises helped make ophthalmology an independent
specialty; Theodor Meynert, an eminent neurologist and psychiatrist who made many investigations on the anatomy and physiology of the brain; Josef Hyrtl, who was the first great teacher of
topographic and regional anatomy; and, finally, Gerhard van
Swieten, founder of the old Vienna School of Medicine.

The likeness of Ignaz Philipp Semmelweis appeared on a
Hungarian stamp in 1932 in honor of his epochal discovery of
the value of antisepsis in obstetrics. This theory first met with
considerable derision, but it was eventually accepted, enabling
it to revolutionize the practice of obstetrics. Another brilliant
investigator, whose portrait was reproduced on a postage stamp
by Czechoslovakia in 1937 on the occasion of the 150th anniversary of his birth, was Johannes Evangelista Purkinje. He
observed that field of different color and equal brightness become
unequally bright when illumination is decreased in brightness.
To the layman, however, he is of interest chiefly because he estab-

lished the permanent character of the fingerprint. The 19th century is known for the investigations of various pathologists, notably those of Louis Pasteur. In 1922, the 100th anniversary of the birth of Pasteur, the French government decreed that the three most used denominations of stamps would bear his profile, and this practice was continued for 10 years. Again, in 1936, a special set of stamps was issued to raise funds for impoverished French intellectuals, one of the stamps showing a three-quarter portrait of Pasteur holding a test tube.

Although some nations have dedicated postage stamps to physicians because of their medical accomplishments, others have memorialized them for achievement in other spheres of activity. In this connection, Germany has commemorated Johann Wolfgang von Goethe, the great 18th century poet who became interested in evolution and who was the first to use the term morphology, and Friedrich von Schiller, who spent so much time writing poetry while he was an army surgeon that he was arrested and condemned to write only medical treatises. Schiller escaped medicine by running off, thereafter devoting himself entirely to poetry, a field in which he acquired immortal fame.

Among "political truants" from medicine are physicians whose likenesses on stamps point to their ability as presidents of nations, high officials in government, or martyrs in the fight for freedom. To name a few, there are such notable American figures as William Henry Harrison, ninth president of the United States, who was a onetime pupil of Benjamin Rush, and Manasseh Cutler, honored on a United States stamp not so much because he was a good physician but because he was a good diplomat, lawyer, and minister of the gospel. Their appearances on postage stamps took place in 1938 and in 1937 respectively. Another medicopolitical figure, who once practiced medicine in New York and who later dominated French politics during World War I, was George Clemenceau, and still another was Sun Yat-sen, who became the first provisional president of China.

The medical history of the United States is replete with names of physicians who have achieved world fame. By means of the postage stamp knowledge of their accomplishments has been spread throughout the land. Among these doctors are Walter Reed, who headed a mission that eradicated yellow fever in the

United States and West Indies, if not throughout the entire world; William C. Gorgas, who made the building of the Panama Canal feasible through the conquest of malaria and yellow fever; and Crawford W. Long for his pioneering with ether as an anesthetic. At the present time American postal authorities are believed to be considering a series of stamps honoring distinguished American medical men. Although as yet there is no intimation from official sources as to the time the stamps will appear or if they will be issued at all, the physicians nominated for the proposed series include, among others, William Beaumont, whose investigations on the digestive process have been hailed by some as America's greatest contribution to experimental physiology; Joseph Goldberger, a pioneer in vitamin research and responsible for the discovery that pellagra is caused by diet deficiencies; William Stewart Halsted, first surgeon to use rubber gloves and a pioneer in the use of local anesthesia; Oliver Wendell Holmes, poet, essayist and critic, who was one of the first to recognize the contagious nature of puerperal fever; William Henry Welch, pathologist and bacteriologist who helped found the Johns Hopkins Medical School; William Osler, whose textbook on medicine is still a standard; Ephraim McDowell, who performed the first ovariotomy; James Marion Sims, father of gynecology; and Howard T. Ricketts, the pathologist, who demonstrated the transmission of Rocky Mountain spotted fever by ticks and typhus by lice.

One of the earliest European countries to recognize the achievements of the nursing profession philatelically was Romania. In 1906 a stamp appeared that showed Queen Elizabeth as a nurse administering to a wounded soldier. The message beneath the Queen's handwriting read, "Wounds are dressed and tears are wiped away." In 1925, stamps issued by Luxembourg depicted a nurse applying medication to the brow of an obviously appreciative male patient. In 1921, Jugoslavia issued semipostal stamps for the benefit of invalid soldiers. One of these portrayed a nurse giving succor to a wounded soldier. On the occasion of the 75th anniversary of the Red Cross movement, a number of countries commemorated the event in stamps. France and Belgium included in their commemorative set a portrait of Florence Nightingale, founder of modern nursing as we know it today.

For the avid medical philatelist there are a number of specialties coming under the general heading "Medical Stamps" that are sufficiently complicated to challenge his ingenuity. Thus, for example, the specialty of the doctor portrayed can be used to establish subclassifications of groups such as surgeons, internists, ophthalmologists, histologists, and bacteriologists. Moreover, a number of geographical features have been named for the medical great, and medical events have been the basis for several commemorative issues. Then, there are stamps dealing with medical mythology, medical buildings and sanitoriums, medical botany and pharmacology, and diseases. All in all, the joys of medical philately are endless, providing both pleasure and education in medical history for those who are drawn to the world of stamps.

Trends in Authorship

ROBERT S. ALEXANDER, Ph.D.

A MAJOR TREND in the organization of science during the past two decades has been an evolution away from the individual investigator in favor of research teams. Accompanying this trend, scientific publications have become afflicted with an increasing tendency towards multiple authorship of papers. Almost any scientific journal will reveal this affliction. In the case of the journal Circulation, volumes 3 through 6, covering the years 1951 and 1952, included 348 papers, of which almost one third (106) had four or more authors. Of these, 35, or 10 percent of the total, had five or more authors; five papers had seven or more authors. These percentages were intermediate to the findings in the American Journal of Physiology, volumes 167 to 171, which yielded 17 per cent of 397 papers having four or more authors, and the Journal of Clinical Investigation, volumes 29 to 30, which revealed 35 per cent of 337 papers with four or more authors. These figures should be contrasted with those for the first 10 volumes of the American Journal of Physiology (1898–1903) in which not a single paper having more than three authors could be found, and the first six volumes of the Journal of Clinical Investigation (1924–1929) in which only five per cent of the papers had four or more authors. Circulation Research is too much in its infancy to yield valid statistics, but it is of interest that 27 per cent of all manuscripts so far submitted to the editor have had four or more authors. Is this trend necessary or desirable?

At the risk of being presumptuous, we would define the requisites for authorship of a scientific paper as being "the contribution of creative thinking to the advancement of science." Creative thinking assumes (or at least should assume) its greatest importance in the design of an experiment. How many creative

Reprinted from CIRCULATION RESEARCH
Vol. I, p. 281–283, July, 1953

minds contribute to the design of the usual experiment? No data are available and generalizations are hazardous, but it seems a reasonable guess that a distinct majority of experimental designs are the fruit of a single creative mind. There are certainly some instances where two or three individuals, who have worked as colleagues for a significant length of time, can design experiments on the basis of discussions in which there was mutual participation. But how often does the basic design of an experiment represent the product of six to eight individuals thinking in unison?

Creative thinking may also be involved in the analysis of experimental results. Here there is definite justification for co-authorship, since the bias or blind-spots in the interpretation given data by an individual investigator may be avoided if two or three competent individuals sit down and debate the significance of their laboratory findings. On the other hand, there must be something drastically wrong with a set of data if their interpretation requires the mutual effort of six or eight investigators.

One source of multiple authorship doubtlessly stems from the growth of research teams, composed of several senior investigators representing different disciplines of science. When it comes to designating authorship, we see no reason why all members of the team should necessarily be included. Publications from such a group are commonly divided into a series of papers focusing on various facets of the broad project, facets which often correspond with the center of interest and the discipline of one or two members of the team. Again the question of creative thinking should be raised, and care taken to see that creative thinking is not confused with expert consultation. Thus the roentgenologist who advises as to the suitable type of roentgenographic technic to employ, the pharmacologist who advises as to optimal dosage of a drug, the physiologist who recommends the proper recording method, the biochemist who details a routine extraction procedure, and the statistician who selects the proper tests for evaluating the significance of the data are acting as consultants. Their detailed technical recommendations, valuable though they may be, should not be confused with true creative thinking.

Another major source of multiple authorship resides in the practice of awarding authorship to junior members of the team who have served in a purely technical capacity. In the performance of such technics as Van Slyke analyses of blood gases, considerable skill is required for precise work, but this technical skill cannot be considered creative thinking. Neither are the activities of the staff member who supervises the Van Slyke technicians to be classified as being in the creative category which merits the awarding of authorship. In a few instances, we might concede some justification in awarding authorship for technical skill, as, for example, in the performance of skilled surgical procedures. To award a skilled surgeon with credit for creative endeavors, however, does not imply any concessions in regard to the assistant who provided retraction for him. The not uncommon practice of awarding authorship to technical assistants who possess advanced degrees, while withholding it from assistants lacking such degrees, may find a ready explanation in the misplaced emphasis on mere numbers of publications in the professional advancement of individuals. Such a basis for determining policies regarding authorship, however, does not do credit to our profession.

Denial of authorship does not necessitate denial of proper credit to other members of the team. One means of awarding such credit is through the usual "acknowledgement," but objections may be raised to this form on the basis that it is obscured by being placed in small type or being buried near the end of the paper. An alternative is to place prominently on the title page, beneath the author's own names, the names of their collaborators with a suitable caption, such as: "With the surgical assistance of ——"; "With the roentgenographic advice of ——"; "Aided by the physiologic collaboration of ——." Where a larger research team is concerned, this may be identified by some such form as "With the collaboration of the staff of ——." More frequent use of this form would be more informative for the reader and convey a higher degree of intellectual honesty than is implied in the indiscriminate listing of all names as authors.

Questions are often raised as to what position the director of a department should assume in connection with authorship of work done by his staff. There are those who espouse the philosophy that the director is ultimately responsible for all the work which comes out of his department, and that, therefore, he should formally assume credit as a co-author. It would seem to us that the creative yard-stick should still be applicable. In some instances, a staff member may serve as little more than a super-technician for his director. The director presents him with a detailed experimental design, analyzes the data as they accumulate, gives instructions that seem indicated for modifying procedures, and at the completion of the project writes up the paper. Here there can be no doubt as to the director's claim to authorship; it is rather the staff member's position as author which may be questioned. On the other hand, a director may be privileged to have experienced investigators associated with him, and the director's role may become that of mere approval of experimental approaches conceived by his associate, administering the department so that his associate's work may progress efficiently, and offering criticisms of a completed manuscript when it is presented to him. Not infrequently, a competent associate may start out with an experimental design outlined by his director, and then, by astute observations of experimental results during the earlier phases of the work, the associate may redesign the experiments, so as to convert an insoluble problem into one which yields conclusive results. For the director to claim authorship in these latter situations appears to be little short of piracy. Apprehensions of directors that they might be forgotten in the acclaim awarded their associates is unfounded. Staff members rarely desire to lose, and even less rarely succeed in losing, the stamp of the director under whom they have worked.

The practical difficulties created by multiple authorship are obvious. Indexing and bibliographic services represent one of the most difficult problems in the structure of modern science. Whether one considers a large indexing agency or an individual investigator compiling a bibliography, multiple authorship necessitates an extravagant expenditure of valuable time and effort, which might otherwise have been devoted to more constructive endeavors.

Of even greater importance is the degrading effect that multiple authorship has upon the meaning of authorship. It would seem safe for the reader to assign a significant degree of credit to the author's name that appears first. In some instances, the reader also may be able to identify the name of the senior investigator in the laboratory of origin, and rightly or wrongly, assign him some credit for the publication. What of the rest? Just what is the reader supposed to deduce from the fact that John Doe was the seventh out of eight authors? This deduction becomes all the more difficult if the reader discovers that the work reported could easily have been accomplished by two competent investigators in two or three months' time.

Instead of being a means of giving credit for creative endeavors, it is evident that there is a tendency to degrade authorship into a form of menial patronage. Multiple authorship could be controlled if editors were to lay down rigid rules restricting the maximum number of authors which would be tolerated, except in unusual circumstances. Such a policy we would hesitate to endorse, first because it appears to usurp a prerogative of the authors, and second, because it would raise the delicate problem of ruling on the exceptions. To achieve a correction of this situation through voluntary restrictions by the authors themselves, it will be necessary for all research groups to subject their policies of authorship to a critical appraisal. A reversal of present trends will require the stringent elimination of the practice of carelessly offering co-authorship to one's colleagues as a token for small services rendered in the conduct of research.

Showmanship in Medical Teaching

WALTER FREEMAN, M.D., Ph.D.

A good teacher is often a good actor. Using the tools of the
showman he can capture his audience and imbue students
with his own genuine enthusiasm.

THE SUCCESSFUL TEACHER must catch and keep the interest of
his student audience. If the audience is attentive, ideas may
be conveyed more easily. All great teachers have some histrionics
about them. John B. Deaver, my professor of surgery, is a good
example. None of the students who attended his Saturday afternoon operating clinics at the Lankenau Hospital is likely to
forget the figure of the man as he held aloft the surgical specimen
he had just removed from the patient and proceeded to point
out just where the offending organ was at fault. He was an easy
man to imitate, since he went through his discourse with measured words, classical gestures and convincing solemnity. On occasion the solemnity was brightened by an aphorism, often of his
own coining. From him I learned such phrases as: "The eye
on the end of the finger." "The surgeon," he often said, "should
have the heart of a lion, the touch of a woman and the constitu-
tion of a mule."

Like an actor, a successful teacher develops certain idiosyncra-
sies that set him apart from his colleagues. He may affect loud
ties or a carnation in his buttonhole, or even grow a beard. An
old rattletrap of a car may be just as ostentatious as a super-
duper. Of course, a younger teacher may consider it poor taste
to vie with his elders in this respect, but imitation is the sincerest
form of flattery. Mannerisms are equally the stock in trade of
the actor and the teacher. In speech and even more in gestures,
the teacher-actor conveys his message to the audience.

Reprinted from THE JOURNAL OF MEDICAL EDUCATION
Volume 28, pages 31–35, January, 1953

LECTURING TECHNIQUES

The formal lecture is the easiest way of transferring information from the notebook of the professor to that of the student, but the teacher who wishes to hold the attention of his audience will speak without notes but with emphasis, pauses, gestures and demonstrations to prevent that stifling boredom that comes over the student.

Allan J. Smith, my teacher of pathology, was one of the gentlest, most lovable of men, always brushing cigarette ashes off his coat and talking as though arguing quietly with himself. He believed in lantern slides and for an hour and a half he would keep up his gentle communing with them, arguing back and forth and drawing on his vast experience. When examination time came around, I argued with him unconvincingly that the cirrhotic liver he presented to me was an enlarged spleen. And it took me eight years to break the conditioned reflex he had established of closing my eyes and going uncomfortably off to sleep as soon as the lights were turned out for *any* lantern demonstration. I came so near failing that course in pathology that it acted as a challenge and for 10 years I was a pathologist. It's only fair to say, however, that Smith took me under his wing the summer following that near disaster and taught me by personal contact what he had so signally failed to present in interesting fashion during the course.

CASE PRESENTATIONS

A good teacher is equipped with a certain dexterity. This applies not only to manual dexterity, particularly regarded by surgeons, but also to verbal dexterity. I speak here particularly of clinical teaching. The teacher becomes a showman when he leads the patient to do the talking. Some patients may be ill at ease, resentful, even hostile at being presented before a group of medical students. The good teacher then reveals his verbal dexterity by putting the patient and the students equally at their ease with a friendly and sincere approach to the problem of the moment. Variety is essential to dexterity. One patient may be presented with light-hearted gaiety that would be quite inappropriate for a patient in the grips of a depression. Some patients expect to be insulted and will not feel comfortable until this has been done. Others will become resentful if any doubt is thrown upon their veracity.

My aunt, the daughter of a doctor, used to say years ago that she wondered where all the nice young doctors came from, since she couldn't endure the attentions of medical students. Probably these young doctors learned a special brand of manners from their teachers.

Dexterity in the field of personal relations is particularly valuable to the student who goes on the wards to find out the nature of the patient's real concern. I recall my embarrassment after I had supposedly worked out a fine case for the chief on medical service and had gained considerable knowledge concerning a trying domestic situation in the life of a young girl, only to find that she had failed to mention an anal fissure that was much more distressing to her than a frustrated love affair.

There is a facility for the communication of ideas that comes to the rescue of the student and the young physician when he can see the patient put at ease and in a frame of mind to discuss the things that really trouble him. This communication cannot occur in the presence of antipathy, ridicule or hostility. Shame of itself need not be a bar to such communication. In fact, the telling of a shameful episode sometimes acts as a release and by this means useful rapport is established.

AUDIENCE PARTICIPATION

Audience participation is part of the dexterity exercised by the good teacher. There is entirely too much passivity, too much spoonfeeding still in our medical schools. We teachers talk and demonstrate and arrive at conclusions and ask for questions —and end the session without the least idea of what the students are really thinking.

Scolding, ridiculing and criticizing are ways of raising a barrier between teacher and student as well as between clinician and patient. Only when a certain comfortable rapport is established can ideas begin to flow. This does not mean that errors should be overlooked, and an occasional egregious one may well be brought to view for the benefit of other students. It is well, however, to have it out on the floor of the classroom rather than to reserve the matter for settlement after the class is over. One of the great thrills experienced by a teacher is to witness the dawn of comprehension that steals over the countenance of the students when the presentation has succeeded.

Audience participation favors the flow of ideas because interest is aroused by a divergence of views. Arguments are useful, particularly if there are two or more possible interpretations to be placed on a given set of facts. The art of diagnosis consists of drawing correct conclusions from inadequate data. Consequently, there are plenty of facets that may be argued with more or less convincing enthusiasm, and everybody may be wrong. This is the strong point of the pathologist to whom all opinions must be yielded in the long run. The point is that the good teacher takes a stand and interprets the findings in as direct and practical a way as possible, on the lookout for what Harold Stevens has called gram-negative herrings. If his conclusions turn out to be erroneous, he can quote the learned judge who is reported to have said: "This court is often in error, but never in doubt."

Manual dexterity is another of the good teacher's talents and it should be cultivated. I try to impress upon my students, some of whom will become teachers, that they should master some particular technic. It may be as simple as a cisternal puncture or a carotid injection, but it should be done with such ease and precision that others will comment upon it. If the student acquires mastery of a certain technic in this way, he will be known as an expert in the field and in related fields.

Teaching of manual dexterity requires close supervision at first and encouragement later on. Then when the student is well on the way to competence and at the point of being able to profit from some of the fine points, the teacher should put on the gloves himself, as it were, and do the next case with all the dexterity at his command.

DEXTERITY IN DRAWING

Dexterity in drawing on the blackboard does not come easily, but the teacher with ability will be able to convey his ideas much better by a rough diagram on the blackboard than by the most finished chart that can be reproduced by the projector. The teacher will hold the attention of his students if he builds up on the blackboard something they can recognize and appreciate. It is particularly the evolving process, the establishment of the aspects of the objects he is seeking to demonstrate one after the other that holds the attention.

This aspect of teaching requires a certain dexterity that must be cultivated like the playing of a musical instrument. The teacher who anticipates a lecture with a blackboard will do well to put in a half hour or so of practice beforehand. I learned this from my professor of anatomy, George A. Piersol, who cultivated his gift for illustration with chalks of different colors. At the blackboard he seemed ambidextrous and not infrequently would draw simultaneously with both hands. It was probably the beauty and clarity of his diagrams of the nervous system that inclined me toward neurology from the first year in medical school. Before each lecture, however, he would spend the better part of an hour familiarizing himself with the feel of the chalk and the proportions of the blackboard. The students profited more from this than from looking at the handsome drawings in his textbook of anatomy. "Now this little aperture at the apex of the cochlea is called the helicotrema," he would say. And the spiral of the cochlea and the phantom of the labyrinth would grow as from a nebula upon the blackboard. It was more than interesting. It was fascinating.

AUDIOVISUAL AIDS

Elements which cannot be presented satisfactorily by blackboard drawings lend themselves to a choice of audiovisual aids. The dullest are tabulations; the most vivid are sound movies. The presentation of such materials is of great importance, since even the best table can be devitalized by too much compression. Simplicity and directness are the qualities to be desired. The test of showmanship lies in the presentation of the data in such a manner that the student will carry away an impression of the fundamentals instead of being perplexed by trivialities.

Among such aids, the photograph is of considerable importance. It is well for the teacher himself to be on the spot with a camera when unique events occur that will serve as useful illustrations in teaching. Some years ago I discussed my views on the subject of physical exercise in the treatment of hypochondriasis.

The point of the talk probably would have been forgotten completely but for a photograph of a woman who had taken my counsel to heart and had developed back and arm muscles that put her into the class of lady weight-lifters.

Before-and-after photographs are of exceptional teaching value and should be taken repeatedly and filed for future reference. The teacher who makes his own photographs has a means of communication that is exceptionally stimulating. He knows because he has seen, and he can teach because he has recorded. One picture is worth a hundred words; two are worth a thousand.

Color photography has been simplified to the extent that even the rank amateur can get good pictures by following directions, and color makes a psychological third dimension. Color movies with sound are the acme, but because of expense are likely to be used only for special studies. However, there are a number of film libraries where interesting productions can be obtained for small rental, and since part of the showmanship of teaching lies in the variety of presentation, such movies are well worth using.

DEMONSTRATIONS

Demonstrations are sometimes simple, sometimes complex, but their value does not depend on this quality. Sometimes a very simple illustration can put across a big idea. My former assistant, Dr. Oscar Legault, showed me a trick illustrating the effects of a blow on the head. He first held up two eggs. They looked the same, but when he spun them one revolved much better than the other. That one was hard-boiled. However, when both were spinning and he touched them lightly, the cooked one stopped immediately, while the uncooked one continued to spin. This illustrated better than any number of words the concept of the jelly-like brain within its hard container.

Demonstrations at the operating table seem likely to come back into vogue now that infectious complications are traced so rarely to outside contamination. With the use of sulfa drugs and antibiotics, the surgeon need no longer fear the presence of students, and his teaching may be made more forceful when he actually demonstrates what there is to see. Granted that surgical technic cannot be learned by looking over a surgeon's shoulder, nevertheless there is something vital in seeing a chest or abdomen opened and the living viscera exposed. The relationships can be demonstrated much more clearly than they can by lantern slides.

Television of operations has acquired a merited success and has achieved marked popularity at various large medical gatherings. It will be some time, however, before the importance of this medium in the teaching of medical students can be evaluated properly. The surgeon operating in such exciting surroundings is justifiably under tension, particularly if something goes wrong. Once when a clamp slipped and the aorta began to gush during an operation for stenosis, the audience went away with the famous last words: "Cut that damn thing off!"

CONCLUSION

Showmanship in medical teaching consists in using certain skills in a convincing way and keeping the audience interested. Chaucer wrote of one of his Canterbury pilgrims: "And gladly would learn and gladly teche." I would emphasize the word "gladly" for it is the enthusiasm of the teacher that communicates itself most vividly to the student.

ART AND SCIENCE

---13---

The Pitfalls of Clinical Research

C. L. BUXTON, M.D.

M ANY CONTROVERSIAL and contradictory conclusions occur these days in connection with every type of medical research. This is particularly true in the field of clinical endocrinology, a field in which results are unusually hard to evaluate in absolute positive or negative terms. The reasons are probably several.

In the first place there is a habit amongst clinical investigators in this field, probably more than in other specialities, of drawing definite conclusions from the ephemeral and indefinite evidence of symptomatic change. Unfortunately, there is a wide "twilight zone" in the area of truth when positive statements are made on the basis of patients' symptomatic reactions, since these reactions can so easily be interpreted according to the expressed or subconscious desires of the investigator. A good example of this is the familiar and all too frequent type of investigation which reports the effects of therapy upon such conditions as the menopause or dysmenorrhea. The usual technique is a very simple one. Individuals complaining of what the clinician considers to be symptoms of the menopause, for instance, are given treatment with a certain kind of medication and are later questioned as to whether or not these symptoms have been relieved. The procedure frequently acquires the cloak of scientific dignity by the use of a collateral series of controls with a placebo. The question of whether or not the actual symptoms from which the patient is suffering are due to the condition being treated is frequently not gone into very seriously. In this instance the multitudinous symptoms from which patients suffer at the time of the menopause are frequently considered to be due to estrogen deficiency. This may possibly be so, but except for vasomotor instability,

Reprinted from THE JOURNAL OF CLINICAL ENDOCRINOLOGY AND METABOLISM, Volume 13, pp. 231–233, February, 1953 there is not a shred of evidence to indicate that it actually is the case. Therefore, when it is stated that relief of these symptoms is due to estrogen replacement, definite conclusions are being made from very indefinite evidence—certainly a *post hoc ergo propter hoc* type of fallacious reasoning.

A second intellectual hazard for most of us is a great tendency to generalize from specific instances. Herein lies the great danger of drawing conclusions from case reports. An unusual and interesting case is cited wherein, following a certain type of therapy, a patient undergoes a dramatic, spectacular and beneficial change. The implication is obvious that all patients who are suffering from this abnormality should then be given this medication. This type of reasoning occurs very frequently in connection with problems concerning the treatment of sterility, anovulation, and menstrual abnormalities. Everyone who is involved in the investigation and treatment of sterility problems becomes more and more aware as the years go by of the many tangible and intangible variables which occur in this condition. Nothing could be more fallacious than to suggest the general application of a type of therapy because it happened to have been successful in one case. This type of reasoning was proved to have been false about two thousand years ago, and there is no reason why it is not just as false today.

As if these were not sufficient reasons why the literature in connection with endocrine and sterility problems is controversial, there is one other unusual difficulty in connection with this specialty which always must be considered. Whereas, in certain types of medical investigation, the results of animal experimentation can be transferred almost directly to the human, this is not the case with endocrine research. Most animals and humans react very similarly, for instance, in the field of immunology; and investigation of surgical problems can be carried out very advantageously in many animals, even though anatomically they are not necessarily exactly similar to the human. In the field of endocrinology, however, there is an amazing amount of species specificity. The pituitary-ovarian-endometrial relationships, for instance, vary tremendously as one advances up the mammalian scale, from the non-menstruating, easily ovulating lower mammals to the complex, little understood "menstruating anthropoids" and humans. One has only to cite the difference in the effect of chorionic gonadotropin on the ovary of small mammals and of humans to give an indication of this great variability. Many other instances could be cited: the difference in the effect of estrogen upon the pituitary of the rat as compared to its effect in the human; the production of fetal resorption or abortion following excessive estrogen dosage in animals, compared to the present (possibly erroneous but apparently harmless) technique of using excessive estrogen dosage in humans for maintenance of pregnancy. These are but a few examples of the fallacious results which would occur if animal experimentation in this field were applied to the human being.

Many years ago Roger Bacon devised what he called "Four Stumbling Blocks to Truth." They are:

1. "The Influence of Fragile or Unworthy Authority."
2. "Custom."
3. "The Imperfection of Undisciplined Senses."
4. "The Concealment of Ignorance by the Ostentation of Seeming Wisdom."

Possibly, if we clinical research workers review in our minds these and other pitfalls and jealously guard our basic motivation —which is to add to the general fund of useful medical knowledge—there will be less controversial and more truthful material in our medical literature.

14

Creativeness in Medicine

ALAN GREGG, M.D.

W ELL, HERE YOU ARE, after fifteen or twenty years of education, with habits of work and study already formed, with ideas and ideals already established—perhaps, indeed, inveterate—long since accustomed to yourselves and the values and beliefs engendered by your experience. Though change in your ways is still possible, it would scarcely be likely were it not for one priceless characteristic possessed by probably all the higher vertebrates and scientifically shown by Pavlov as the conditioned reflex. That magnificently heartening phenomenon offers us all escape from the life of a foreordained automaton, from habits that deaden, tastes that cloy, and a routine that has gone stale, jejeune, and tiresome. Thanks to that delightful ability to attach a new meaning to an old or hitherto meaningless stimulus, man possesses something akin to rebirth, to the forgiveness of sin, to the opportunity to change and grow, rechanneling old energies in directions quite new.

Still deeper than this encouraging plasticity lies the fundamental fact that so complex and unique is each one of you that I could not expect that any one system of education or any one set of experiences could by now have either stimulated or satisfied all of your potential capacities or latent desires. As a consequence, you are still ready to begin new quests; you are prepared for a commencement. Mere experience and habit—especially if they have been accompanied by resignation or cynicism—have already, perhaps, determined what you will make out of the next fifty years. That could be the case, but nonetheless there remains the exciting chance that you can change, the lovely chance that tastes and desires that have never yet been quickened in you, or

Graduation Address at the University of Texas Medical Branch, Galveston, June 5, 1953.

Reprinted from TEXAS REPORTS ON BIOLOGY AND MEDICINE
Volume II, pages 440–447, Fall 1953

your ways of living so that they will be consistent with your convictions. In that task you just can't help being personal and original. As Paul Valery observes, with quiet finality, "Il faut vivre comme on pense: si non, tât ou tard on finit par penser comme on a vécu." "You must live as you think: if not, sooner or later you'll end by thinking as you have lived."

Creation shares with metabolism a quality of hidden selectivity. It is not just swallowing experience but converting parts of it: not merely acquiring information but achieving a transformation of it. Converting an M.D. into a real doctor is a slow process, for learning calls for getting rid of old attitudes as often as it calls for acquiring new ones. That task will prove sober but exciting; a hidden process but, like successful metabolism, observable to everyone in its results; sometimes a real strain but eventually a triumph.

I can't tell you what to be: you already are. Each one of you, by heredity, by experience, by education, presents, like the patients you will be responsible for, an absolutely unique combination of a myriad of traits and abilities and tastes. All anyone could offer to your peculiar and variant characters will be in essence the raw material from which you'll choose what to take in and to transmute in the individual task of creating yourself. Your future is going to be a state of becoming, not being. When becoming stops, you are dead.

Why do you find this talk on creativeness in medicine so unconventional? I think you would have, as medical students, rather good alibis to the charge of ignoring till now the creativeness of medicine. You began your study of the living—with the dead. Your first patient was a corpse—not much of the spirit of creation there. This introduction was to what had been and long since had ceased becoming. Embryology with its enthralling changefulness may have supplied a brief interlude, but soon began a long apprenticeship to tissue uniformities—of composition, of structure, of function, of response to stimuli, and the grim finality of irreversible reactions. Little of creation there. Description was the tool you plied conscientiously for some two years before narration became a second and less familiar key to unlock the realities of patients' lives. Your thought became centered around repair, recovery, return. You were schooled in humility before the finalities of life. But was there enough emphasis on life's spontaneities, its adaptabilities, its variability and mutations? So much of given facts, so much memorizing—little that's Dionysian there! Perhaps you found some relief in the parts of preventive medicine and public health that are not concerned with solemnly locking the stable door after the horse —perhaps a Pegasus—has gone.

So I would not wonder if you are surprised at the suggestion that there's much for doctors to reflect upon in the theme of creativeness. Think of Christ's comment on His purpose: "I am come that they might have life and that they might have it more abundantly." There's room for medical creation in those words— "have it more abundantly." If your patients are to have life more abundantly because of your character, then it will pay you to wonder what hinders and what aids your own growth and development as a person.

The chief hindrance to creativeness is the lack of convictions big enough and deep enough to give a lasting pattern to your professional life. Don't plan your future like a pontoon bridge, each petty span no longer than its predecessor—"the vain repetitions that the heathen use." Decide upon fewer arches and bigger ones. Prefer the longer span—the larger symmetry. Keep in mind a symphony; don't be tied to the tiresome reiterations of a popular tune.

The greatest doctors I have known have shown serenity, a serenity that comes only from clear purposes and a firm reliance upon their tenacity to accomplish them. I venture to call your attention to this characteristic of serenity. It comes from a steadiness of conviction, not from frenetic assertions or impassioned credos. There's much in living that cannot be put in words or formulas. Thinking is a part of living: and the whole can never be contained by one of its parts. Learn to avoid overthinking everything you do—but nonetheless remember that unless you have some steady pattern to your existence it will be hard to avoid what Mrs. Wharton neatly calls "getting into the thick of thin things." And strong as your opinions may sometimes be, it may pay you to keep in mind Oliver Cromwell's advice to his zealots: "Gentlemen, I beseech you by the bowels of Christ to remember for just one moment that you may be wrong." Or, as an alternative to so stern a warning, you may take pleasure in the definition of a zealot as one who redoubles his efforts when he has lost sight of his aim.

Since doctors so often live by patients' confidence, and confidence is the natural child of prestige, the besetting sins of many a doctor become prestige hunting, professional jealousy, and nursing self-pity. Watch out for these, keeping in mind the mellow Chinese proverb that observes "Great men never feel great: small men never feel small." Or, if you prefer advice from Shakespeare, "Ne'er prefer your injury to your heart, less you bring it into danger."

To counteract the hindrances to creativeness in medicine there are aids to creativeness. I have never known anyone who impressed me as a real person whose world did not seem very real indeed to him. It may be a three-ring circus, or it may be another Golgotha—or anywhere between. But in any case it is a real place, with issues and action that matter. When Carlyle was told that Margaret Fuller had decided to accept the World, he grunted "By Gad, she'd better!" At the bedside of disease, patients do not want and do not need to be attended by mere Quiz Kids—persons as miraculous mentally as they are immature in every other way. That is what I mean when I say there are plenty of M.D.'s in this world but not enough real doctors. In the effort to take the world as a real place and not evade its reality you may on occasion find wisdom in the art of timing, in taking advantage of the fact that life ebbs and flows, that the work of the world, like the work of the heart, goes on by means of diastole as well as systole, that children pass through phases, that enough is enough, that a sense of humor and proportion has its uses as well as being perfectly delightful, and that "good horse sense is the sense that horses have, never to bet on human beings." For you will be let down in the most awkward ways. The elder Walpole had a formula for living that you may find useful: "Good sense, good humor, good manners, and good faith." And there's an antidote for self-pity in Christoper Morley's statement that any man who is worth his salt has by the age of 45 acquired his crown of thorns: the problem is to learn how to wear it over one ear.

But the greatest aid in creating yourself may come from

cultivating the art of criticizing yourself. What is the best school of medicine in the world today? There's a delicate reflection! It could be here, but only by your own resolve, for the best school is that whose graduating class not only knows how to criticize themselves but succeed in holding to themselves the magic mirror of humility incessantly, forever interested in learning. Statistically speaking, the chances of this in any one school are small. But the charm of being an individual is that you don't follow statistics: you make them. The chance may be small, but it is yours.

Learning from whom? Learning from every possible discipline and source. That is the purpose of a university education—to draw from each the best that he can give and, with that rarer grace, to take as well as to give. There is no wisdom in deliberate withdrawal from the thoughts, the companionship, and the company of men who wish to know, to find first principles, to reason, and to share their gains. Osler used to urge doctors to take part in their county medical society meetings for the same reason: to reinforce the urge that all of us have betimes to be as the Passavant Hospital motto says, "More than yesterday, less than tomorrow." Never underestimate your need for the company and the companionship of men who want to learn. And above all have the grace to admit that you can learn. Charles Darwin once observed that in his experience men differed more in the degree to which they used their abilities than in the sum total of their abilities. There lies the path to a creative life: using all that you have and thus getting still more to utilize and glory in.

No school of medicine is worthy of the name that does not teach its students how to learn from experience as well as before experience, how to observe and reason wisely, and to compare their work with what has been observed and thought elsewhere, by others and in other times. He teaches best who shows his students how to learn; not what to think in 1953, but how to think, and how to learn to think, in that long stretch of days awaiting you till, let us say, the year 2000.

All these things are but methods and materials. Yours is, and must be, the creation and the synthesis. It will be yours, nor anyone's so much as yours. With all the methods of diagnosis, the instruments and drugs at your command, now and in the future, there still will come that crucial moment when you will be the main medicament, the surest comfort, and the brightest hope of every patient, sick or convalescent, who is yours. Don't forget: make today the commencement of the task of creating the doctor you have planned to be and seek forever to improve that plan.

15

Variation on a Theme

NANCY PROCTER-GREGG

W. S. GILBERT professed dislike of Shakespeare, and was particularly irritated by *Hamlet*. The latter indeed was his
King Charles's Head, cropping up through allusion and analogy
in unexpected places throughout his works, and responsible
incidentally for one of his jokes which has passed into our
speech, when he said to Tree of his performance that he 'never
saw anything so funny in my life, and yet it was not in the least
vulgar'. He made two determined direct attempts to dismiss the
haunting theme, in the skit *Rosencrantz and Guildenstern*, and
the comic opera *The Mountebanks*. In the former, which reads
drearily today and can hardly have been entirely redeemed by
the author's gusto when taking part in it in private theatricals,
Ophelia vents Gilbert's impatience with Hamlet's soliloquies
and magniloquence, and the English reverence for the play, by
tricking him into presenting a 'damned' tragedy written long
before by Claudius but received as a farce; in penalty for which
he is banished to be a bore in England, and Ophelia is free
to marry Rosencrantz. The Mountebanks exhibit Hamlet and
Ophelia as their prize clockwork figures, and when by magic two
real characters are transformed into the automatons they regard
it as great nonsense that the girl should have to commit suicide
because her lover will not marry her when, after all, he wishes to.

These unsatisfactory attempts to dispose of the matter illustrate merely the exemplification in Gilbert of a psychological
truism—he, too, 'protests too much', and shows affinity by his
preoccupation. But in another, and a very fine, work he hit on
the humorous approach to the theme of guilt tragically embodied
in *Oedipus Rex*, *Hamlet*, and *The Brothers Karamazov*, in the
progression traced by Freud; and happened to stage neatly a
dramatization of the latter's technical theory of humour itself.[1]

Reprinted from INTERNATIONAL JOURNAL OF PSYCHO-ANALYSIS
Volume 34, pages 142–145, Part II, 1953

Of all the Gilbert and Sullivan operas, *Ruddigore* 'dates' least, and from the time of the first post-war generation it has grown in estimation. Book and score each show their composers at their best, and the marriage of talents is here conspicuously successful. The libretto sparkles with wit, and the music shines with feeling; as their biographer Hesketh Pearson acutely observes, Sullivan's view that there is no such thing as humour in music was an important factor for the success of his collaboration with Gilbert. We may alter the emphasis of the further conclusion: that had Sullivan seen the possibilities of humour in music he would have failed to illustrate the humour of Gilbert's words, for the reason that he would have demanded a far greater freedom than Gilbert's libretti gave him. Gilbert himself emphasized that the same humour always struck them in the same way: 'With Sullivan I never had to do that fatal thing—explain a joke'. The deep unconscious affinity implied here begot their perfect joint production of comedy, wit, and humour (in the technical meanings distinguished by psycho-analysis), with, in particular, the delicately-adjusted contribution of music to the pathos always inherent in 'humour'. Had Sullivan been a so-called witty musician, the affinity would have been missing; it was not merely that he 'triumphed in interpretation', but that he shared in the creation. Both men unconsciously knew humour for a serious matter, though each consciously longed for his *oeuvre* to be valued most on its literally serious side, in works produced, we may note, independently of each other.

In *Ruddigore* no direct parental complications are evident at all. Sweet Rose Maybud, the heroine, was 'hung in a plated dish-cover to the knocker of the workhouse door, with nought that I could call mine own, save a change of baby-linen and a book of etiquette'. The accursed line of Ruddigore itself has descended from an uncle to the two brothers, who with their alternating renunciation and resumption of the fatal ancestral heritage, interplaying with the 'natural man' role of the invulnerable but ridiculous foster-brother, present an impeccable picture of sibling ambivalence.

The opera opens in the early nineteenth-century village of Rederring (the prevalence of the initial 'R' is curious), where the anciently-endowed chorus of bridesmaids is idle, since even

ose Maybud will declare no choice. Will not her adoptive aunt,
ame Hannah, take old Adam? Nay, says the Dame, for she is
ledged to eternal maidenhood—and she sings the Legend of
ie Witch's Curse. Sir Rupert Murgatroyd, the first Baronet
f Ruddigore, ruthlessly tortured witches, and one of them cursed
is line to the effect that each lord of Ruddigore must commit
t least one crime every day for ever, or himself die in torture.
In Gilbert's stage directions for the later array of ancestors, Sir
Rupert is of 'the time of James I'); in *Rosencrantz and Guilden-
tern,* Gilbert remarks of Hamlet:

> 'Whether he's dark or flaxen—English—French—
> Though we're in Denmark, A.D. ten-six-two—
> He always dresses as King James the First!'

Hannah had been betrothed to the last holder of the title, Sir
Roderic, but on discovering his identity of course renounced him,
nd he 'died but ten years since'.

Now Ruthven, the elder nephew, has in fact evaded the terrible
necessities of his succession, and is living in the village disguised
is a farmer, Robin Oakapple. He is in love with Rose, but both,
is they explain in a charming duet, are too diffident to declare
hemselves. Robin's foster-brother, Richard, turns up from a sea-
ight, where his ships actually fled from 'the darned Mounseer',
although Richard ascribes that course to magnanimity (a joke
which gave some offence, wryly enough, to the French component
of the first-night audience; we may remember that the English
and the Jews both have the reputation of being able to laugh
it themselves, and in this the very English Gilbert and the partly
Jewish Sullivan may have shared some relish).

Richard promises to 'speak up' for Robin to Rose, but in the
ensuing passages falls in love with her himself, and secures the
promise of her hand—but Robin, re-entering, is emboldened
to declare himself, and after showing up Richard for a coarse-
fibred if lovable lout, compared to his supposed farmer-self,
seems for a moment likely to pluck the fruits of his 'family
romance' without incurring the penalties of its realization.

At this point, however, the stage is cleared for the entrance
of Mad Margaret. According to Gilbert's stage-directions, 'she is
wildly dressed in picturesque tatters, and is an obvious caricature

of theatrical madness'. Conformably to Gilbert's own detaile
management of productions, the Savoy presentation always show
her as Millais's well-known portrayal of the drowned 'Ophelia'–
red hair, nightgown, and all. Her babblings, in fact, have
horridly genuine ring; we are reminded of Hamlet's

> 'It is not madness
> That I have uttered; bring me to the test,
> And I the matter will re-word; which madness
> Would gambol from.'

Her short scene always induces some discomfort in the audi
ence, comparable to that of certain analytic hours, but relieve
by the bland if imbecile common sense displayed by Rose May
bud. She is, of course, mad because she loves the present ba
baronet, Sir Despard. She strews Ophelia's weeds, and has a
moving ballad about a violet 'in a nest of weeds and nettles
who hoped that the lover would gather her—but 'he gathere
for his posies Only roses—only roses!' The wicked Sir Despar
enters, with chorus of Bucks and Blades, and explains his fright
ful dilemma. Threatened by his picture-gallery of ancestors, he
commits his crime each day, but for the rest of his day he doe
good; he steals a child and builds an orphan asylum, robs a
bank and endows a bishopric, means to carry off Rose Maybud
and atone with a cathedral (!).

In a very witty scene, crowned by a duet and pastoral chorus,
Sir Despard learns from Richard that Robin is really his elder
brother Ruthven, and exposes the latter, who assumes (in a
literal alteration of costume and lighting, and always drawing a
laugh) his mantle of guilt; Rose renounces Ruthven, and Despard redeemingly turns to Margaret, while Richard embraces
Rose, and the Act terminates with the 'Happy—' tune of the
finale—but Ruthven is left with his burden of guilt.

The second Act is staged in the picture-gallery of Ruddigore
Castle, with the ancestors looking down. A matured and haggard
Sir Ruthven discusses his criminal programme with his steward,
the old Adam. Richard and Rose solicit his permission to marry
and—influenced by the Union Jack and the ties of foster-brother-
hood, and knowing his own position hopeless—he yields. Left
alone, he considers his week's tally of feeble crimes, and wonders

'Will my ghostly ancestors be satisfied with what I have done, or will they regard it as an unworthy subterfuge'? They, in turn, all sickened of guilt and called on death for release; he begs them for pity. The stage darkens, and when it becomes light again the pictures have become animated, and the ancestors in solemn chorus step from their frames, anathematizing their trembling descendant. Last comes Sir Roderic—'Alas, poor ghost!' cries Ruthven.

Sir Roderic has a famous song—the Ghosts' High-Noon. Into this, with its haunting, rousing melody and weird falling cadences, Sullivan poured his genius. When the opera failed to attain the instant enormous success of its predecessor *The Mikado,* Sullivan blamed the resurrection in the ghost-scene and Gilbert blamed Sullivan for not treating it humorously enough, saying the ghost music was like introducing fifty lines of *Paradise Lost* into a farcical comedy. They were both right in recognizing it as the emotional climax of the opera, which distinguishes it from the others and lifts it, probably, to a more permanent height of aesthetic achievement.

The essentially tragic impression, revealed by the music, of Ruthven's conflict with these formidable superegos is brought into relief by a brilliantly funny dialogue between Ruthven and Roderic about his week's 'crimes'. The ancestors, of course, are dissatisfied, as Ruthven knew they must be; he has not lived up to the obligations laid upon and fulfilled by them. The mild masochism of his crimes against himself, such as forging his own will, provides no avenue of escape from the 'original sin' imposed upon the Murgatroyds by the witch's curse. He must commit a real crime; must, say, carry off a lady. He refuses— and the ancestors by pointing at him induce the penitential agonies, too great for him to bear. He yields, and in a final chorus the ghosts—a nice touch!—demand and receive his pardon before retreating to their frames.

The wretched ego, reconciled thus miserably with his masters, sends the old Adam off to carry off 'a maiden . . . anyone—I don't care which—', and we are treated to the appearance of Despard and Margaret, happily united and redeemed from their guilt and madness, and clad in puritanical black as the reformed preceptors of a National School. Funny as this scene is, it displays remarkable psychological insight into an uncomfortable corner. Margaret, who has known what it was to become mad through love of a forbidden object, still has 'odd thoughts'— 'and I sometimes think that if we could hit upon some word for you to use whenever I am about to relapse—some word that teems with hidden meaning—like "Basingstoke"—it might recall me to my saner self'. Despard uses this bit of obsessional ritual with success—Ruthven makes the mistake of trying 'Birmingham', and Margaret herself corrects him. This apparently senseless joke became famous at once amongst Victorian audiences who reckoned to know 'hysteria' when they saw it.

The purpose of the visit is to persuade Ruthven to defy his ancestors and abandon his evil courses. He agrees, and in a brilliant 'patter-trio' to the theme of 'It really doesn't matter!' the three of the younger generation, with that resigned humour which is born among the difficulties and inconsistencies of the nursery world, resolve to accept things as they are.

But Ruthven, left alone, is appalled by the reappearance of the old Adam—'the deed is done!' He has carried off the maiden, in the person of Old Hannah, Sir Roderic's pledged love. She is infuriated, and Ruthven terrified. She 'produces a very small dagger'; but this she throws to him, and takes 'a formidable dagger from one of the armed figures' in the ancestral portraits. The classic unequal combat—always greeted by roars of laughter —can have but one outcome. Ruthven, routed, makes a desperate appeal: 'Roderic! Uncle! Save me!'

Sir Roderic makes an impressive entry. (The original stage-directions were that he should rise from a trap, and the scene did not make the impression Gilbert intended. We do not know how far he was conscious of the dominance of the *Hamlet* motif, which apparently has not attracted comment in connexion with this work; at any rate he seems to have discarded the 'cellarer' analogy without hesitation when the emotional effect of his conception could be better served by a dignified stepping-down from the portrait frame.) When he sees who it is, Sir Roderic exclaims 'Little Nannikin', and Hannah replies 'Roddy-doddy'—and everyone is put in his place at once. Ruthven is sent out of the room, and Roderic and Hannah have a pathetic 'Lack-a-day' ballad, which, with its exquisite modulations into the minor key, has melted hearts from that day to this. They embrace, Hannah in tears.

The dilemma seems insoluble, but upon this scene Ruthven bursts, making the classical child's interruption. Sir Roderic and Hannah are properly annoyed, but Ruthven 'can't stop to apologize—an idea has just occurred to me. A Baronet of Ruddigore can only die through refusing to commit his daily crime.[1]

> *Sir Roderic:* No doubt.
> *Sir Ruthven:* Therefore, to refuse to commit a daily crime is tantamount to suicide!
> *Sir Roderic:* It would seem so.
> *Sir Ruthven:* But suicide is, itself, a crime—and so, by your own showing, you ought never to have died at all!
> *Sir Roderic:* I see—I understand! Then I'm practically alive!'

The menacing yet rescuing super-ego has in turn been bested and rescued by the ego. Between them they have seen the joke, laughed off the burden of guilt, and there is room for everyone to live happily ever after.

The oedipal spectres will gather again in the consulting room; the tragedy of the Brothers Karamazov is more frequently encountered than the humour of the Brothers Murgatroyd; the English answer to the great riddle may be uttered more profoundly by Bunyan, when Christian's burden at sight of the Cross slips from his back and 'the springs that were in his head sent the waters down his cheeks'; yet as the curtain falls on *Ruddigore* we know that we have had an agreeable reminder of the message of humour as noted by Freud: 'Look! This dangerous world—this is all it is. Child's play, so we may laugh at it!'

REFERENCE

1. Freud, S.: 'Dostoevsky and Parricide' and 'Humour', *Collected Papers*, Vol. V. Hogarth Press, 1950.

16

The Therapeutic Art

JOOST A. M. MEERLOO, M.D.

THE ART OF THERAPY involves more than applied scientific deduction. That is why I will try in this essay to analyze some objective and subjective motivations that influence the medical art.

A deplorable difference exists between the physician who cures and the scientist who makes a diagnosis only. When the acute emergency of a disease forces immediate intervention, the diagnostic intellect hesitates while the therapeutic and helping instinct often acts even before thinking.

The medical student is aware that he is chiefly taught extensive diagnostic knowledge, but he is not given much instruction about the art of therapy. He must teach himself that therapeutic ability later. A synthetic science of the therapeutic arts does not even exist at present; pharmacology, immunology and surgery are only specific physical and chemical introductions to such sciences of therapy. Systematic psychotherapy is just in its beginning. Because we still lack a general science of therapy, medical science is burdened with a tragic conflict that may lead to therapeutic nihilism. This is certainly not the aim of medicine. Many a young physician, as well as the public, speaks with disdain of ampules, powders, pills, lotions and ointments. He is derogatory of operations or analytic treatments. The public, with its naive criticism or affirmation of various kinds of therapy, forces many doctors to act according to its wishes. The drug manufacturer often tries to suggest to the physician what his future therapeutic action should be. This strategy is often more pronounced in the non-official and pseudomedical schools and among quacks and shamans who utilize our lack of systematic study of therapeutic methods to introduce their magic skills. Much of the therapeutic reaction will depend on the subjective attitude

Reprinted from POSTGRADUATE MEDICINE
Volume 14, pages 458–464, November, 1953.

of the doctor toward his patient and on the latter's need for intervention, thus forcing the doctor to follow certain lines of therapy. Modern psychology knows more about this mutual relationship between doctor and patient. Many patients get better only because they wish to please their physicians or because their physicians please their neurotic needs.

When the physician asks himself if it is time to act, to do something in addition to the *vis medicatrix naturae*—the natural curative forces—he studies pathologic symptoms and other indications that will determine therapy. Nature has presented the symptoms of illness; now comes the therapist to alleviate the illness. The physician places *skill* and *science* in opposition to the processes of disease.

Bleuler[1] in his book on medical thinking asks if this kind of immediate therapeutic thinking is right. The physician's question implies that he wants to give treatment per se without asking himself if such intervention is really needed. Almost no physician exercises *udenotherapy* or gives placebos on behalf of conscious medical abstention. Most patients would not allow it. Our therapeutic activities even make real knowledge of disease more and more difficult, because in actual life we now rarely encounter untreated symptoms.

The medical school teaches many definite indications of specific treatments. Not being mature in his medical thinking, the student must follow these teachings or risk error. This educational suggestion gives the idea of a stable form of pathology that does not agree with the ever changing picture of reality.

Is the definitive therapeutic indication wrong? No, we need this form of well defined medical prescription in emergency cases, but the belief is wrong that only one way of action is good in each case. However, with our science of therapy just beginning, we must not expect to learn an unambiguous therapeutic truth—an impossibility in a science of life.

What does therapy mean? The therapist looks for a certain directive plasticity in life that will offer a basis for change in the sick process of the human being, so that the therapist may be able to lead the pathologic development into new and healthier ways of life. This can be done in one of two ways. The morbid influences—noxious facts—can be eliminated or neutralized; we may speak in this way of an antinoxious therapy or antitherapy. But the other way is also possible; to correct and stimulate the living autarky of our psychosomatic structure, e.g., to stimulate the inner curative processes and defenses. I propose to speak in this case of a constitutional therapy or protherapy. In daily medical actions, we always find a combination of both principles.

Sometimes the school may teach treatments which fail completely in practice. At other times, there are confusing differences of opinion. That the student wants well defined indications and directions is good, for without them he would be confused and hesitant in the midst of manifold opinions.

There is only one person to whom this therapeutic dilemma does not matter—the patient himself. He does not belong to any diagnostic school nor does he prefer any therapeutic rule. He is just a human being who lives once and uniquely in spite of all scientific ruling. He wants to be helped; that is all!

Every therapeutic decision is essentially an opinion of one individual about another. The doctor decides with his acquired sets of opinions and prejudices and the patient reacts with his preconceived expectations and needs.

How is the sharp scientific therapeutic directive born? Whenever the rationale of our treatment is at stake, we cannot escape some thinking about the methods we use.[2] I propose to make a division into scientific, suggestive and subjective directives. The *scientific indication* is generally accepted; it is the result of analysis of many facts, so that its logical conclusions cannot be denied. The *suggestive* indication comes from the picture presented by the patient—his attitude, a certain striking symptom, or his subjective needs which force the doctor into a certain therapeutic act. The suggestive indication is dependent upon the patient or his environment, his cults and sophistications. The *subjective* indication comes from the doctor: his personal attitudes, his conscious and unconscious motives decide his form of therapy.

1. THE SCIENTIFIC INDICATION	Experimental indication
	Statistical indication
	Historical indication

2. THE SUGGESTIVE INDICATION   *Indicatio vitalis*
                                     Social indication
                                     Monosymptomatic indication

3. THE SUBJECTIVE INDICATION   Transference and counter-
                                     transference
                                     Indicatio "utque fiat"
                                     Indicatio "pro domo"

THE EXPERIMENTAL INDICATION

This program of scientific action is a result of that part of the medical science that at present is held in most esteem. The scientist asks Nature a question by means of experiment and uses the answer to determine further action. An example of such experimental indication is the treatment of serum allergy. If it becomes necessary to inject therapeutic serum, after having formerly used serum from the same animal on the patient, it may be expected that the patient has become allergic. Instead of one direct shot, the fractioned dosage of Besredka may be used. This method results from answers to questions concerning therapy the scientist has asked of Nature, i.e., the guinea pig. The experiences from animal experiment are thus transferred to clinical use for man.

This method assumes that Nature is able to give a single answer to a question. Medical theoretical thought is guided chiefly by generalized causal thinking—that every special case is part of a generally valid law. In practice, however, experience proves that there are no simple generalizations in therapy. We always find changed circumstances because of certain individual and constitutional factors. As an example, although we are familiar with the soporific action of barbituric acid, in some patients with brain disease these drugs act paradoxically and cause excitement instead of sleep.[3] The difficulty in therapy is to compromise between known general biologic reactions and the unique individual constellation and reaction. Every therapy moves between generalization and individualization.

THE STATISTICAL INDICATION

From a variety and multitude of former experiences, we wish to establish a therapeutic directive for the future. A majority of useful therapeutic experiences establishes the expectation that we will meet with the same success in succeeding cases. That is why the scientific critic always asks for large statistical figures when evaluating therapeutic success. We may call this the dictatorship of numbers. However, when one studies the history of medicine, and the reports of impressive results in large numbers of patients with medicaments that are now obsolete, one concludes that something is wrong with our comfortable statistics. Nothing has changed as much through the ages as therapeutic success; after great success, the new cure disappears into oblivion.

In the first place one often forgets that psychosomatic man and his changing and growing structure cannot always be utilized in statistics. It may be that within a few years his pattern of reactions will have changed completely. Collective changes and expectations will play a role in this. For example, after a cerebral accident, man's pharmacologic sensitivity and toxic vulnerability will have changed.[4] Furthermore, not enough attention is given to the fact that in biology one well studied case sometimes can teach us more than many therapeutic successes studied more superficially. Each case is a meeting point and cross section of manifold general laws.

Besides this, how difficult it is to interpret statistics! And how easy to give them a favorable aspect! How many statistical figures are launched to serve the honor or prestige of a certain clinic! There even exists a special technic to "correct" therapeutic statistics and to eliminate the bad factors.

Every newly discovered medicament means a revolution in therapeutic habit formation. In the beginning the new drug cannot do much better than the older ones because we have no statistical comparisons. I do not speak about those fascinating discoveries proving immediate new results (antibiotics, ACTH). But here, too, there is the tendency to generalize their use as an arcanum and we lose statistical and therapeutic insight. Another determining factor in statistical results is the group of patients who provide the material for the study. Most definitive therapeutic indications come from medical schools and university hospitals. But in those clinics a special social group of patients is chiefly treated. In Western Europe there is even more difference. Usually, only the poor visit the university hospitals. Many physicians have found again and again that the "golden" private practice has a different basis for psychosomatic reactions. The sensibility and vulnerability of a well trained laborer are different from those of an old, inbred family. That is important in surgery. We find in biology that in a too differentiated and refined organism there is less ability for regeneration. Surgical success, after all, is the result of spontaneous regeneration of the organism, besides the well applied technical skill of the surgeon.

From the clinic we want statistics of facts, the social reaction of the patient and the mind of the scientist who observes. However, at the same time we want observation of single cases, for they teach us the variability of the reaction of life. Let us look at a few examples:

Modern surgery of the sympathetic nervous system teaches us to heal with success some forms of intolerable pain. This kind of therapy will be more difficult to apply when the mental reactions in patients are more subtle and complicated. As soon as the pain means neurotic conversion, surgery, however suggestive it may be in the beginning, only helps temporarily. These forms of continual pain may be treated better with psychotherapy. There may be some pain, brief but so intense that it becomes a new, morbid emotion for the patient. I once treated a patient with trigeminal neuralgia, who never overcame the painful trauma of the now old-fashioned alcohol injection of the gasserian ganglion. The injury of the operation seemed to be more catastrophic to him than the old neuralgia.

Eugenics is a part of medical science which tries to prove, with figures, the usefulness of certain preventive measures. For example, it wishes to prevent the procreation of inferior genes by sterilization of human beings. I have two criticisms in relation to the mechanical side of this argument. First, the young science of genetics has until now only been observed for three generations of human beings in order to come to a certain conclusion. That is not enough for the discovery of valuable genetic rules in man. But there may be something that evades the tentative rule of genetic science, and that is the spontaneous and unique biologic development. One usually studies what can be causally

and statistically interpreted and only that part can be suppressed
by means of sterilization.

THE HISTORICAL INDICATION

This therapeutic directive is the beloved child of old clinicians.
When the experiment cannot direct or prove our way of action
and when even the statistics cannot give any positive suggestion,
then most clinicians revert to the revelation of old clinical bedside experience. There is something of a mystic trust in historical
facts and a magic aura around old medical prescriptions.

The historical outlook always gives a long section of medical
experience! Because their own era is too confused, many seek
further truth in past experience. It is true that in medical practice
clinical experience with drugs has taken place mostly before
pharmacology was able to give reasonable explanations for its
therapeutic results. That is why historical study is still able to
offer many new approaches to therapeutic problems. There are
many examples of this: Quinine, arsenic and mercury came to
our medical arsenal long ago. We find many other old medicaments whose exact pharmacologic actions are still obscure, such
as Kal. jodetum, arsenic, strychnine, salicyl, etc. Gradually, however, the newer pharmacology gains ground and will be more
able to direct the uses of drugs.

THE SOCIAL INDICATION

Man is simultaneously an individual and a member of a group
or community. To cure a human being means not only to help
him in the struggle against natural disastrous forces but also to
fit him for certain social tasks and adjustments. Man, the individual and the member of a social organism, needs the help of
that organism, as a plant needs its roots.

Disease is never a purely biologic reaction; it is also a failure
to adjust to social life and is always associated with the struggle
for life. Because of the difficult struggle for life, the physician
often must choose a form of therapy that considers the special
social and economic situation of the patient.

Especially in psychiatric diseases do we need this social
approach. The mentally ill person is known as someone who is

harmful either to society or to himself. He suffers from inner or outer forces, dependent, of course, upon the mental and social habits in his group.

In modern therapy more attention is given to the social validity and adjustment of patients. Modern therapy of fractures is directed to obtain restoration of function as soon as possible, in opposition to the old surgical therapy which gave more attention to anatomic repair. Some forms of treatment of tuberculosis, for example, artificial pneumothorax and thoracoplasty, are usually done in relation to the functional cure and mental activity of patient, contrary to the long rest cure in a sanatorium. Modern drug therapy again has changed this therapeutic behavior; extended treatment in a hospital or a sanatorium may make an unsociable being of the patient.

The different social security laws have effected a change in medical motives. In some cases the physician must be a kind of detective in order to be able to select the imagined complaints from the real symptoms of disease. Instead of diseases he has to treat the wish to be sick or the wish to escape into the protective disease. My experience is that this psychologic knowledge leads too much to a certain suspicious approach on the part of the doctor toward the social security patients. Real simulation of disease after an accident is seldom seen. In the army, many a physician tended to develop the same aggressive, suspicious attitude toward victims of battle neurosis. Every doctor is unconsciously afraid of his own infantile wishes, and this makes it difficult for him to evaluate neurotic symptoms objectively.

THE VITAL INDICATION

The emergency signal sounds! When the signs of death threaten, every therapist hesitates a moment. No matter how scientifically we can influence a biologic occurrence, we cannot conquer eventual death. When an emergency forces us to act to prevent impending death, we want a clear indication how to act, how to lengthen life, before using more complicated methods. Such is the doctor's religion, his belief in the sacredness of life itself.

In acute lethal danger nearly all therapy becomes rather simple. It is as if, in the moment of danger, clashing medical opinions meet. We apply cardiotonics, transfusions, tracheotomy, etc. before the more causal therapy is used, because life must not escape us, *Ars longa, vita brevis,* Hippocrates taught us, and the good moment passes soon.

In acute danger every doctor is glad to have a clear pattern of action; the therapeutic activity helps him to conquer the general human fear of death. In this area the competition with quacks and mystic therapy suddenly disappears.

THE SYMPTOMATIC INDICATION

All kinds of primitive and archaic opinions still live in the midst of scientific medical thought and they continually influence medical action. In archaic times, symptoms of disease were explained as localized demons against which were used exorcisms, magic spells or offers of appeasement. Demons were also banned in a more active surgical manner by *ferrum caudens.* Even now, medical science must fight against the old demons and ghosts, but in a more hidden way. The old thought association—symptom—antisymptomatic medicament—still exists. The layman especially asks the doctor to follow this procedure. The primitive belief in miracles assumes that no disease exists without a counter medicament. Such thinking of course leads to a polypragmatic therapy that can be compared with the application of the miraculous arcanum in the Middle Ages, so-called Teriac—a mixture of innumerable magic substances—which served to cure all kinds of symptoms.

Nevertheless, symptomatic therapy can be important if therapeutic science fails and if one is able to relieve and to alleviate suffering. In this connection we should mention the narcotic drugs. When they are used well, they belong to the best means of symptomatic treatment mankind possesses. What physician would want to work without them! But subconsciously the drug fortifies the suggestion that an outside medicament can expel the inside demon. The same narcotics can play havoc with the human being, can enslave him and bring him closer to the uncontrolled fantasies of primitive people.

Even surgery is scientifically described as symptomatic therapy. Surgery also expels affected parts of the body which have become dangerous or without value because of pathologic processes. Surgery interferes with biologic processes which cannot be influenced by physiologic therapeutic means because of lack of sufficient medical knowledge. That is why the ideal of good surgery is to make itself superfluous.

TRANSFERENCE AND COUNTERTRANSFERENCE

There is a continual and mutual relationship between doctor and patient. The patient wants his physician to be a god, a magician, a miracle worker. When he trusts his doctor, he subconsciously feels that every medicament has magic curative powers. The doctor needs such a transference from his patient. It is more than 50 per cent the secret of his cure. One doctor is better able than another to provide such transference. In everyday practice we call it "bedside manner" or "therapeutic instinct." The psychologist assumes that in this doctor-patient relationship all sorts of earlier relationships in the patient's life are repeated. The doctor must be aware that in every sick room, during every disease, the old drama of the helpless child in a hostile world is repeated and the physician represents the almighty parent who gives new power and confidence for the future.

But every relationship is reciprocal and the doctor also transfers to the patient his miseries, his sorrows and his hopes. The patient influences him. That is why he may fail because, due to unconscious reasons, he is not aware that he may be neglecting his patient, or that he is falling in love with him or her and that he feels confused because of this. As a result, the prescribing hand may write the wrong formula!

There is a vast range of subjective feelings between doctor and patient. Sometimes the patient wants the doctor's suggestions very badly because of their "magic" action, as is true in hypnotherapy. Sometimes the doctor communicates to the patient things he does not believe himself, but which he thinks are good for the patient. Although this happened more when medical psychology was not as well developed as it is today, this simple form of bedside psychology is still in use. Think, for example, of that innocent bottle of medicine, the placebo. According to scientific rules, it does not act pharmaceutically, but the patient swallows a spoonful of consoling suggestion every two hours. This kind of old-fashioned suggestion is often used in therapy. The general practitioner evades the real psychologic situation that would bring him and the patient nearer to the basis of the complaints. Instead, the doctor treats these with a pharmacologic lie. But I must say those suggestive medicaments help the simple-minded, and what philosopher does not become simple-minded when he is ill!

In former times, physicians prescribed rather drastic medicaments because of their suggestive action, such as asafetida. In modern times, it is done more elegantly with all kinds of nerve tonics, hormones and vitamins—the manifold, magic medicaments for nervous complaints. The choice is usually dependent upon the therapeutic mode and the influence of the local drugstore.

It isn't always the patient who asks for such an easy, acceptable suggestion. Often the doctor has to calm parents or frightened relatives with such prescriptions or other forms of fascinating treatment. Modern therapy helps him with glamorous and glittering electronic machines to sustain the suggestion. A tremendous resistance exists against rational therapy; the public wants magic machines!

THE "INDICATIO UTQUE FIAT"

A well known practitioner told me, with a large degree of self criticism, that 90 per cent of his therapy occurred as follows: The patient asked for something; the doctor's medical skepticism delayed a decision, but his prescribing hand was already moving. The other 10 per cent of his patients urged him to think about their real medical problems. These patients did not ask for immediate therapy. Especially during consultation hours, large numbers of patients force the doctor to use this reflexive prescribing hand. In the beginning, he may resist such action, but later he begins to believe in his automatic writing. This is a scientific danger—the belief that no disease is allowed to exist without medical intrusion.

The *indicatio utque fiat* paralyzes true medical experience.

THE "INDICATIO PRO DOMO"

Medical action loses its objectivity when motivated by personal longings and subjective tendencies. We have seen the examples already in the process of countertransference. I do not like to underline here all the faulty motivations found in myself and in my colleagues, for I am sure that we detect the same egotistic factors in other professions. But, in the medical profession, it is often easier to hide private emotional investments behind pseudo-scientific, noble justifications. Sometimes a new, valueless therapy is started in hope of stimulating personal fame. At other times, we evade theoretical difficulties by oversimplification of therapy. How many neurotic conversions have lost their organs and not their disease on the operating table? Specialization has had a bad influence on our general medical view, because every specialist is influenced by his particular scientific and economic interests. We must be aware of the fact that, in our therapeutic directive, unconscious motivations may influence our thoughts. These may be not only hidden, aggressive or sadistic traits, but also unconscious needs to be a healer and a god—as impractical and deceiving as unconscious sadism.

The patient too may suggest very interesting, inopportune treatments—a miraculous therapy, for instance, in order to become famous in the family, or his masochistic needs seek mutilating operations or depriving diets. Here we arrive gradually at psychopathology.

Enough of therapeutic directives! There are moments when the doctor becomes conscious of the motivations that lead to his actions. Yet there is still no therapeutic discipline that guides us against all the confusing and seducing suggestions of everyday life in the realm of treatment.

If we realize how exact our diagnostic knowledge already is, and, at the same time, if we realize what a difference there is between scientific diagnostic knowledge and therapeutic art, then we know how grateful we should be that medical schools provide us with a minimum number of clear therapeutic directives.

Nevertheless, at every moment on our way to better science we must look back with a critical view, for without this we become "polypragmatists," who fall for every new suggestion. We must realize that in every practical case we must depart from our scholastic precepts and individualize each case. For, in practice, we must treat patients and not schemes. Objective scientific indication will remain, because it will always relate personal therapeutic art to impersonal science. Human contact with the patient and the impersonal appraisal of scientific knowledge must together form what one may call the real medical art!

REFERENCES

1. BLEULER, E.: The Autistic Undisciplined Thoughts in Medicine. Berlin, Springer, 1922.
2. MEERLOO, A. M.: Patient and disease. An excursion on medical thinking. Z. Neur. 131:556, 1931.
3. MEERLOO, A. M.: The action of barbituric acids. J. Ment. Sc. 26:1, 1933.
4. MEERLOO, A. M.: Variable tolerance to alcohol. J. Nerv. & Ment. Dis. 105: 590, 1947.

17

Caritas Medici

WILLIAM BENNETT BEAN, M.D.

T̲HE OCCASION of the installation of an Alpha Omega Alpha chapter is a fitting time to take a broad view of some of the central problems of morals, ethics, and humanities in medicine. This honor society, emphasizing scholarship, has grown in stature because it recognized students with especially high qualities. It is an honor to present this address and I begin it by congratulating your Alma Mater on this symbol of excellence and you who have been chosen to uphold what should be every physician's ideal "to be worthy to care for and heal the sick."

II. A dozen themes crossed my mind as possible topics for my talk, and I have chosen one made up of Latin words because it not only defines the mores of the physician of good will but embodies a rich expression with the savor of the early morning dew still upon it. The expression bedside manner, more sinned against than sinning, captures some of the meaning. *Caritas* through vagrant changes gives us charity and care and carries implications of love and tenderness and dearness. But *caritas medici*, a physician's *caritas*, means more. It is that vigilant and humane insight and care, compact of wisdom, and spirit, which the doctor owes his patient, be it for discipline or sympathy. This concept Francis Peabody epitomized beautifully for us in his statement that "The secret of the care of the patient is in caring for the patient."

III. One of the rare major intellects modern medicine has produced, Wilfred Trotter, has given me a theme. He says:

The passage of time has tended more and more to clear up these lingering confusions of an anthropocentric biology, and thought is gradually gaining

An address delivered in Oklahoma City, May 1, 1953, at the installation of a chapter of Alpha Omega Alpha of the Medical School of the University of Oklahoma.

Reprinted from the A. M. A. ARCHIVES OF INTERNAL MEDICINE
Vol. 92, pp. 153–161, August 1953

courage to explore, not merely the body of man but his mind and his moral capacities, in the knowledge that these are not meaningless intrusions into an otherwise orderly world, but are partakers in him and his history just as are his vermiform appendix and his stomach, and are elements in the complex structure of the universe as respectably established there, and as racy of that soil as the oldest saurian or the newest gas.

IV. The capacity to offer criticism and the willingness, one might say the temerity, has become increasingly rare in our age of conformity. I say as did Lord Bacon in his preface to "The Elements of the Common Laws in England" that

I hold every man a debtor to his profession, from the which as men of course do seek to receive countenance and profit, so ought they of duty to endeavor themselves, by way of amends, to be a help and ornament thereunto. This is performed, in some degree by the honest and liberal practice of a profession; when men shall carry a respect not to descend into any course that is corrupt and unworthy thereof; and preserve themselves free from the abuses wherewith the same profession is noted to be infected. But much more is this performed, if a man be able to visit and strengthen the roots and foundation of the science itself, thereby not only gracing it in reputation and dignity but also amplifying it in profession and substance.

V. For those whose cortex is not congealed (and in these humoral days I must specify cerebral, not adrenal cortex), there is fascination in speculating about what future medical historians, say 50 or even 500 years from now will think of us. Each age mercifully thinks of itself as being the best and by definition is the most modern and contemporary. Without being morbid or melodramatic I will point to certain features of modern medicine which should be of special concern to you who by natural endowment or hard work have demonstrated qualities of scholarship and leadership. Physicians as a group are no longer distinguished for their contributions to or knowledge of humane letters. The curious concentration upon accumulating data, the mesmerization in developing techniques, the hypnosis of applying tests, have all inevitably tended to separate the individual physician further and further from contact with the patient. In any art or craft the nearness of the artisan and material is measure of its validity, and in the art of medicine this nearness of patient and physician must be maintained in spirit as well as in substance. Moral values, historically the binding link between the good physician and his patient, have been relegated to a corner or thrown bodily out the door at no little hurt to the proper aim of medicine.

VI. If sudden catastrophe comes and puts an end to our modern society without quite extinguishing it, who will be the Hippocrates or the Galen of the ensuing dreary ages of darkness? What handful of current medical books would you select to dominate by dogma a future when advance is frozen? Or perhaps will the future hold that these, our times, are themselves veritable dark ages, that the concentration on fact and method of the modern conveyer-belt practice of medicine has so depersonalized us that we are not even as humane physicians as were the barber-surgeons of bygone days?

VII. I hold as first premise that physicians and most members of our contemporary professions, by forsaking humanism and the feeling for continuity with history, have debased themselves to the role of technicians in a trade school age. Even without religion and the spirit of wonder which we too often dismiss with childhood, human nature escapes the raw crassness of a molecular vision of man and life if it is imbued with historic sense and humanistic spirit. Secondly, if we have not some creed and acceptance without proof every man is slave to his own intellect. He cannot honestly venture beyond the near reefs of what he himself has proved. Whatever the individual brilliance and talents, the life of man is bounded by pressures and time which do not much exceed the Psalmist's three score years and ten. If modern man must build his own tower, unaided by the past, small wonder that it is often a tower of Babel. We must all take what good and what solace we can from the vast concourse of history to avoid incessant repetition of error long exposed and participation in futile races already lost. Thirdly, I submit that morals and manners are different expressions of the same principle, a principle which though it may not thrive on a base of history and humanism cannot come into being without them. The present-day physician by his training in the laboratory and his devotion to the totems of a "scientific" age risks losing contact with the historic role of the physician. In the rush of everyday work his manners have vanished and he is made uneasy by a dim but haunting consciousness of a want of moral force or moral standards.

VIII. Let us without fear or favor look back at the training of
the medical student of today. His preliminary learning at home,
whatever it may have been, certainly did not include cultivation
of a knowledge of the classics. Very probably there was no deep
spiritual force. The standard education of the grammar school
and the high school or prep school stressed in the great current
American tradition sports, teamwork, cooperation. He did not
get rigorous discipline in any field. Compare the education of
the founding fathers of the republic whose training was designed
to fit them for active participation in the society of the day,
training in the art and science of thinking rather than the
squirrel-like activity of accumulating vast quantities of facts.
Graduation implied mastering the three elements of the trivium,
grammar, logic, and rhetoric, and the four elements of the
quadrivium, the four liberal arts, music, astronomy, arithmetic,
and geometry. Their mastery was tested by the defense of a
proposition or thesis against any and all comers. Think how
far we have fallen from the aims expressed some 200 years ago
about just one of the aspects, namely, competence in rhetoric,
which included

teaching us how to elevate our wisdom in the most amiable and inviting garb
and to give life and spirit to our ideas and to make our knowledge of the
greatest benefit to ourselves and others, and lastly, how to enjoy those pure
intellectual pleasures resulting from a just taste for polite letters, a true relish
for the sprightly wit, the rich fancy, the noble pathos and the marvelous
sublime shining forth in the works of the most celebrated poets, philosophers,
historians and orators with beauties ever pleasing, ever new.

And what does the college training, the preprofessional experience of the physician of today include? A vast concentration on
the sciences, chemical, physical, mathematical, biological, with
a minimum of anything that could be included under the ancient
trivium and quadrivium. In fact, where these arts stand today
is exquisitely illustrated by the scorn we have cast on the word
trivium by our own trivial. Then the training in medical school
with its initial emphasis on the basic sciences delays cultural
growth by not approaching any preclinical field as a science in
its own right but merely as applied to the future training in the
medical school. Finally, by the time the undergraduate medical
student arrives at the bedside it is no wonder that he experiences

great difficulty in thinking of the sick patient as a person at all instead of the cumbersome vehicle of marvelous lesions and curious processes or as a psychosomatic complex. Medical school training could scarcely be less conducive to the one possible salvation at this stage; namely, a true interest in medical history.

IX. And now you are come to the time of graduate training, the internship, the residency, and, for some, fellowships, research, teaching, and for all the final incarceration in the minutiae of practice or administration. What chance is there for you today in our system of collectivist training when we are enthralled by one of the unhappy aspects of our aging and security-minded society, namely the influence of the specialty boards on graduate medical training. My views are sufficiently well known to this audience not to need further elaboration. Therefore I merely comment that it is sad enough to be confined in the miserable cage of conformity but doubly sad that so many are in love with the cage. I for one have not been unmindful of Horace's query, *Quis custodes ipsos custodiet,* or, to paraphrase in the words of a popular song of yesteryear, "Who'll take care of the caretaker's daughter when the caretaker's busy taking care?"

X. With this background little wonder that there is so much emphasis on money, on expensive cars, on a life measured by bank account, television, and a conservative view which is retrograde in outlook and stifles with precocious senility. The vapidity of medical writing which reflects very little logical or rigorous thought indicates that the cultural potential of physicians, instead of leading, has fallen below the average. Anyone forced by editorial obligations to read critically many medical papers is struck by the singular and consistent absence of form, a vast desert of data with the rare oases of prose all too often the dried up water holes of the alkali plains.

XI. And what thesis do I propound from a view of the history of humane letters as it bears upon the profession of medicine today? It is simple. It has no sanctions beyond some familiarity with the accumulated experience of the past. From the Renaissance onward developments in medicine illustrate the extreme difficulty that man has always had when accumulations of facts, the raw data of science, so overload the intellect that logic goes flabby from overwork in systematizing knowledge. Imagination

is shackled, perhaps by fatigue or by not having the time needed
for meditative gestation.   In any event, we have seen the strin-
gency of the austere rationalism of the Middle Ages and the old
urbanity of Greek rationalism fade out before the immense and
monolithic aggregations of contemporary fact.   How truthful
were the words of Artemus Ward—"The researches of so many
eminent scientific men have thrown so much darkness upon the
subject that if they continue their researches we shall soon know
nothing."

XII. Henry Adams is a good example of the disorder of thought
that is inevitable with the deep pessimism of a purely material
concept of life.   To him life was the vaguely disturbing hum
of a top running down.   Compare William James's meditative
view of the significance of the second law of thermodynamics. He
was concerned not so much with the total volume and duration
of energy as with its distribution and the work it produced.   He
readily granted that the destination of mundane travel might be
zero but nonetheless the scenery was magnificent and if the ultimate end was extinction the penultimate might be the millennium.

XIII. Another example of the dilemma of contemporary man
in his efforts to deal with masses of accumulated data is Selye's
Procrustean endeavor to equate disease with stress, for here
surely neorationalism has gone soft with a surfeit of miscellaneous
facts which cannot all be acted upon by intellectual digestive
juices and reduced to a final simple concept.   Not the least distressing aspect is the pessimistic implication of the stress thesis;
namely, that life is disease, since existence without stress is inconceivable.   This implication is none the less gloomy because it
is so subtle.   Is this an unduly somber reading of the contemporary scene?   The world is about us for those to read who
will.

XIV. The fruitful and great tradition of Western society has
been the worth of the individual and the freedom of the soul,
and our society has drawn strength and sustenance from the
inner revelations of saint and artist.   It will continue at its own
hazard if it abandons this source of inspiration for external
manipulation and purely mundane solution of its problems.   The
great leader whose creative personality transforms and elevates

mankind will be increasingly rare in the ordered society we are
entering with its drastic suppression of everything which tends to
escape from the dominant norm of its stereotype. Indeed, in
such a situation, salvation of the individual is replaced by the
security and welfare of the collective or common man. As physicians we risk becoming repair men and mechanics for that bleak
abstraction "The Common Man," whom the small-volt engi-
neers serve up to us as an engine slightly more complex than
their electrical turtle. No hot-brained physicist with his transis-
tors and cybernetics is going to hoodoo *me* out of *my* mind, such
as it is, or, in the words of Walshe,

interpret for me in terms of microvolts and feed-back mechanisms in the brain,
the sonnets of Shakespeare, the Primavera of Botticelli, or the going out to
death of Captain Oates in the dark wastes of the Antarctic. There are more
things in heaven and earth than are revealed by an amplifying valve.

XV. Primitive man, loaded with taboos, blocked in on all
sides by fear and superstition, was finally freed by the emergence
of intellect and the advance of knowledge. Indeed, science itself,
by enlarging the scope of human choice, actually contributes to
human freedom, for no one can choose what he is ignorant of.
As an example from everyday life, the necessity for obeying traffic
regulations is not looked upon as a serious loss of freedom because
of the great potential which is opened up by employing the
paraphernalia of an automative age. I think the prophets of
doom have looked too dimly upon the possibilities of human
intellect and instincts combining for a practical solution of our
problems. But it should be remembered that intelligence leaves
its owner no less impelled by instinct than his simpler evolu-
tionary ancestors. It merely enlarges the capacity for varied
response.

XVI. Somewhere between intelligence and instinct we find
habit, which is most useful because it releases the energy for
intellectual exercise from ordinary matters, allowing it to concentrate on the exceptional, the novel, and the changed. Instinct
is the imbedding of such responses within the genetic mechanism
that controls natural development, but it too, can play a part
in liberating the intelligence from routine. Therefore, properly
adjusted instinct and intelligence may be, and indeed must be,
harmoniously combined.

XVII. My plea is that somewhere into a habit pattern we put good manners and morals, that we recognize not only intelligence and emotions, but, I add and I urge, spirit.

XVIII. Let me wander off into another bypass for a moment. It is not surprising that devotees of the psychosomatic have not seized upon the innumerable references by perceptive writers of the past to illustrate better than most of them do today in what is too often arid and graceless prose the concepts they aim to codify into a new branch of medicine? Smollett in his remarkable book, "Humphrey Clinker," has this passage in which Squire Bramble writes to Dr. Lewis.

I find my spirits and my health affect each other reciprocally—that is to say, everything that decomposes my mind, produces a correspondent disorder in my body; and my bodily complaints are remarkably mitigated by those considerations that dissipate the clouds of mental chagrin—The imprisonment of Clinker brought on those symptoms mentioned in my last, and now they are vanished at his discharge.—It must be owned, indeed, I took some of the tincture of ginsing, and found it exceedingly grateful to the stomach; but the pain and the sickness continued to return, often at short intervals till the anxiety of my mind was entirely removed, and then I found myself perfectly at ease.

XIX. It is curious and disheartening how we have neglected spirit as well as literature all these years. The melancholy absence of spirit from much psychosomatic emphasis today merely exemplifies a general trend. It is tragic that in some places the psychosomatic school, with such potential for good, should have been developed and popularized so much by the nonhumanistic scientist rather than have arisen from a view of the patient which included spirit with mind and body. When medicine was split off from the church, duplicating the old cleavage of physician from priest, the apothecary surgeon had in his care the mind and body. The parson or priest was left with care of the soul, and his employment was contingent on failure of the physician. The strange controversy of science versus religion added injury—as though music was to be judged by the tone deaf or painting by the color blind. The low place accorded to the spirit today is measure of our perverse inability to deal with nonmaterial, nonobjective phases of existence, perhaps a reversion to the conceptual level of matter rather than energy.

XX. As a foremost attribute of spirit I reckon morals and the practical everyday correlate manners. In its simplest aspect physicians encounter it in relations and interrelations with patients. The teacher-student association should sustain the same pattern and ideally so should the investigator-subject relation. With so much science we have tended to relegate the practical arts of medicine to the lowest place on the totem pole. These arts represent a traditional and special body of common sense knowledge in action. As knowledge expands, the general principles governing these arts may emerge and slowly the arts become transformed into applied science. Until this happens their employment is critically necessary. This involves certain intellectual arts. They demand special mental aptitudes, the fruit of training and experience, which show up in the fine clinician as in a connoisseur and in the poor one as in a dilettante.

XXI. I will quote now some paragraphs from a convocation talk I gave several years ago to medical students.

Let your concern be for excellence in manners in dealing with colleagues, teachers, friends, and patients. Undergraduate students have not escaped the corroding blight of modern times and modern education, that of unkindliness and selfishness. In the protracted adolescence of modern society our hunger for pleasure and happiness finds expression in boorishness, vulgarity, and petty meanness which is especially distressing and hazardous in professions concerned with health. It is disheartening to note man's inhumanity to man in any place but it is particularly so where it affects the sick and the miserable. All too often a doctor, a nurse, an orderly or others caring for the sick exhibit meanness, short temper, or maybe just some trifling lack of consideration which may nullify the efforts of brilliant science and technical virtuosity. In manners the simple rule of putting yourself in another's place will indicate what should be done. Thought and consideration for others will alleviate some of the pains of neurotic preoccupation with self which prevails so widely. With the emphasis on considerateness it is even possible that politeness may grow into courtesy and courtesy into the dignity and refinement which constitute excellence in behavior.

In the selection and cultivation of your friendships remember that subtle qualities rather than superficial ones are of importance. To a surprising degree your friends influence you and mold your habits and character. In your associates be content with nothing less than the best. Avoid the flashy, the vicious, and the shallow. Good company elevates whether it be in the people you associate with or in the books you read. Indifferent company is retarding and dulling. Bad company weakens and ultimately cripples.

Another admonition concerns integrity and intellectual honesty. In professions which depend on personal relationships and of course in all others there is no substitute for absolute integrity. A baneful tendency of some of your education up to now has been that as students you have lined up in a hostile and separate camp on the one side, with your teachers and instructors in another, and made sport of getting away with what you could in petty deceits. Dishonesty corrodes. You cannot compartmentalize its sphere and be honest in all save one or a few sections. In learning a profession the substitution of another's knowledge in default of your own is a malignant deceit which may destroy your usefulness because it later endangers those coming to you for help and comfort. In the various branches of the medical and health professions those infected with dishonesty may survive for a time, but sooner or later the blight will damage others and so destroy them.

Among the many problems which concern us, your fellow students, who by accident of chronology happen to be teaching, is the age old problem of the proper balance between education in facts and education in methods, between technics and knowledge, between ways and wisdom. Contrary to what you may suppose, scientific facts are not final and eternal but change with our growing understanding. They are knotty difficult things, and all of us at certain stages must learn a great many of them by sheer force of memory before we can integrate them into the broad pattern of what we are learning. You must never be satisfied with the mere accumulation of facts but rather try to get an understanding of their relations one to another. Be concerned not only in the acquisition of a storehouse of facts, a knowledge of technics, drugs, and doses, but in an appreciation of their true significance as they relate to the various branches of professional activity in which you will be engaged. Unless you achieve excellence not only in knowledge but in the art and craft of a profession, an integration and synthesizing of your facts, it becomes a mere business. The art of what you practice has to do with personal relations, and success in such matters depends on high standards of excellence being kept in view at all times.

How are such standards to be sustained? To recall the aphorism ascribed to Hippocrates, "Life is short and art is long, opportunity is brief, experience dubious and judgment difficult." The time is past when spoon feeding can nourish your minds and give the needed sturdiness to the fabric of intellect and character. There is no magic vitamin, no capsule of intellectual chemotherapy, which will serve in the place of the one medicine which gives excellence—hard work, Dr. William Osler's master word. Work, he says, is "a little word but fraught with momentous sequences if you can but write it on the tablets of your heart and bind it upon your foreheads." And how can work enable you to reach your goals? Most readily by cultivating a system, by concentrating and attending. If ever there was a time of scattered attention this is it. Suspended by vague ambitions, prodded by anxiety and baffled by frustration, we seem to have lost the capacity for sharp and exclusive focus of the attention. Without attention there can be no system, and system withers without work. Remember this, to reach the narrow end of the distribution curve which marks excellence, you must have an abiding conviction of the need for hard work and the value of system in your work.

XXII. There can be no real need to lay qualities one against another, a comparison of those we should have and those we should suppress. In all our dealings we should be calm, not rough. The patient is by definition sick or thinks he is which is the same thing for our purposes. A calm demeanor may help soothe him. Quietness and poise instead of confusion and noise, kindness instead of thoughtlessness, patience instead of hurry, thoroughness instead of superficial approach. These I think all have their counterpart in morals so that honesty, candor, strength, and integrity must dominate the scene.

XXIII. Somewhere during my brief Army experience in the Pacific, I came across a mimeographed sheet of paper with a moving message. The paper, briefly read, has disappeared. Neither the source nor the author is known to me, but I should like to conclude with the words modified as I remember them.

Go calmly amid the daily hurly burly. Remember the peace there is in silence. Be on good terms with people. Speak your truth quietly and convincingly but listen to others; they have their side to tell. Avoid loudness and aggression. Comparisons are to no purpose for there are always greater and smaller persons than yourself. Enjoy your plans as well as your achievements. Keep a vital interest in your own professional life and progress, a real possession in the changing fortunes of time. Do not let dishonesty blind you to the fact that virtue exists. Be true, be yourself, and be true to yourself. Do not feign love, nor simulate affection. Neither be ironic about love. In the face of all disillusionment and disenchantment, it is as perennial as the grass. Grow old gracefully surrendering at appropriate times the things of youth. Do not borrow trouble with dark imaginings. Be gentle. You are a child of the universe no less than the stars and the trees and whether you see it or not no doubt the universe is unfolding as it should. Be at peace with God whatever you conceive him to be. In the noisy confusion of life be at peace with your soul.

XXIV. And finally I end with a quotation from Tennyson's "Idylls of the King," which I think might be as profitable reading for many of us as the latest installment in the mystery of the isotope. I quote:

> For manners are not idle, but the fruit
> Of loyal nature and of noble mind.

ACKNOWLEDGMENTS IN LIEU OF BIBLIOGRAPHY

As the perceptive will see, this paper is derived, and, much more than the quotations indicate, it represents the selective quarrying of other men's minds. That some may be moved to explore the easily found sources I am putting down for reference in a sort of skeletal "Road to Xanadu" some of the paths which have been followed. To my parents, among innumerable debts, I owe the love of reading, a care for fine books, and a fascination with the potential beauties of language as a medium for ideas; to my teachers at Episcopal High School, Williams, Reade, Hoxton, and others, the first love of excellence, avidity for knowledge, and the illumination of the classics, and to Barr, Lewis, Metcalf, Luck, Webb, and others at the University of Virginia the disciplines of scholarship in a university setting where honor was the theme of our common dealings and where Jefferson's influence was pervasive in much more than just the grace and dignity of the beautiful buildings. My medical way-farings, Virginia, Johns Hopkins, Harvard, Cincinnati, and Iowa, of supreme importance, really comprise another story.

I have numbered the paragraphs in order to avoid chopping up the text with distracting reference marks.   ..

II. This theme was taken from F. M. R. Walshe (Arts of Medicine and Their Future [Lloyd-Roberts Lecture], Lancet 2:895, 1951), and some of the words too. His several lucid critiques of the contemporary scene, notably his Harveian Oration (1948) and Linacre Lecture (1950) have been borrowed from freely. Peabody's thin volume, "The Care of the Patient," I find essential reading at least every year.

III. Trotter, in his luminous and sparkling "Collected Papers" and erudite "Instincts of the Herd in Peace and War" has combined deep thought with criticism in a wonderfully elegant and sharp style.

IV. Bacon is just as stimulating and pertinent today as when he wrote, and has much good advice.

VIII. The quotation is from J. J. Walsh's "Education of the Founding Fathers of the Republic."

X, XI. Walshe and Charles Singer have contributed thoughts and some of the words.

XII. Recently published letters exchanged by Adams and James develop this theme.

XIV. The first sentences are almost a quotation from some lost source, and more than the quotation marks indicate came from Walshe.

XV, XVI. Part of this is from the same lost source as XIV.

XIX. This paragraph owes much to George Day's 1952 Hunterian Society Oration "P.P.S." but does not exactly fall within quotation marks.

XX. Osler, Singer, Trotter, and, not least, Walshe had a hand in this.

XXI. In my original convocation talk I acknowledged a debt to Aring and quoted him, but when I later reread one of his papers, which I had heard delivered, I realized how much more was inspired by his ideas and words, which in turn had a debt to Daniel Drake. I have a treacherous memory which may let go dates and doses but fix leech-like on a paragraph or verse.

In the process of recall the verse gets identified but sentences or paragraphs lose their provenance and appear unobtrusively in my writing. Such accretions I have tried to recognize, and to this end I have made a card file of underlined passages from a wide and various reading which now, alas, has grown past my capacity to index it.

XXIV. Guinevere, from "Idylls of the King."

There are influences of Alan Gregg, Mayo Soley, Stanley Dorst, Detlev Bronk, and many others which involve attitudes more than words. Perhaps critical readers will notify me of hidden sources and lost references.